— Derek the Cleric —

A Year at St Cliff's

Andy Robb

CWR

SOME RATHER NICE THINGS PEOPLE HAVE SAID ABOUT DEREK THE CLERIC ...

Keep them coming, Rev. They are brilliant !! Many thanks.

This makes me laugh.

Bless you, you bring a smile to my face in some rather hard times. Thank you.

Great blog.

Defo funny.

Cracked me up.

VERY COOL – JUST SUBSCRIBED!!

It's really quite clever. Good stuff really.

Thanks, Derek. **Keep revin!**

I am still your number one fan.

VERY CLEVER!!

I would love to be a part of your friends list as it is a fantastic way to openly show that us Christians do actually have a great sense of humour.

I put this on my page and the response from friends (even in the States) has been so funny.

Brillant! I must show it to my vicar and the old people's lunch club!!

Well done, Rev. I certainly enjoy being one of your vast number of friends – long may you continue to entertain us!!

Amusing, as always!

You are a legend! Full of wisdom.

Genius! More humour needed in church – thank you!

HA, HA, HA, HEEEEEE!!

Brilliant!!

Keep up the good work.

One of an agreeably large number of those who appreciate your ministrations!

My idea of fun 'n' faith – I am impressed!

How very true, Rev!! Hilarious too!

Well done!

A riot but an original nonetheless!

You always make me smile!

Your best yet, Derek – your reward will be in heaven but please stay around for a long time to continue with this good work.

I lurv your blog.

I wish our vicar was like this vicar.

KEEP THEM COMING ... YOU DEFINITELY BRIGHTEN UP THE DAY.

Great to be in your online congregation.

I am enjoying your comments.

LIKE IT A LOT!

Another marvellous musing. Well done for raising a smile.

Brilliant pictures, you are a clever one.

Mega-funnee :-)

This is so funny I had to share it with my friends.

You made me laugh and that's what I need right now – so thanks.

Awesome.

Derek is Pastor of the Year.

It made me laugh so much.

Hilarious! Go back to the darkened bowels and blow the dust off some more.

Keep going on – we love your take on life ... We must not take ourselves too seriously.

OH, I LOVE THIS – SO FUNNY! :)

Introduction

Dear Friends

A warm welcome to this wondrous tome of mine. I trust that it will not only provide a window into the world of this humble clergyman but also into that of my charge, St. Cliff's.

Who would have thought that my regular ramblings, 'uploaded' onto the 'World Wide Super Highway' (as I believe it is referred to in contemporary parlance), would have led to my gaining immortality within the pages of a book, no less?

Whilst this collection of musings, miscellany and much, much, much more (I fear that my alliterative ability is not perhaps what it used to be) might not quite rival the creative genius of the world's literary greats, I do hope that it nevertheless brings a little joy and lightness to your soul.

Should this publication sell sufficiently, I feel that I will be more than justified in using some of the proceeds to purchase a celebratory packet of chocolate digestives, a personal favourite of mine.

The remainder of the monies, I fear, will have to go the way of Jonah – they are destined to be swallowed up; not by a large fish in this instance, but by that greater and far more all-consuming monster, St. Cliff's ubiquitous (and perennial) Roof Fund.

Within the pages of this book you will not only find an ample collection of my musings which have oft provided regular sustenance to my 'online' congregation (or so I have convinced myself), but also miscellaneous 'bits and bobs' such as a selection of my personal photographs (my good lady wife is to blame for that), clippings from the celebrated St. Cliff's Weekly News Sheet, copious 'Notes to Self' and various correspondence which I felt might be of interest to you.

I trust that you will enjoy my profferings.

Onward and upward

Derek

A Foreword By The Bishop

I have been asked to write a foreword to what I gather is the collected works of one of my underlings.

In truth I have not had the time to indulge in the frivolity of perusing his handiwork, but I will take his word for it that it does not detract from his duties as a parish priest, nor does it stray into the realms of heresy.

That being the case I am prepared to commend this fellow's efforts to you.

Let us hope that you are edified somewhat more than you might be from one of his occasionally passable sermons. Should that be the case, I would imagine that you will have little recourse to a refund.

For myself, I appreciate the receipt of a courtesy copy of this publication by way of recompense for putting pen to paper. After all, it would be highly unlikely that I would purchase one.

I think that is all I have to say on the matter except for the fact that the underling in question has also asked me if I might include in this personal preface mention of the fact that he is not quite a novice when it comes to this writing malarkey. He did once have a short article printed in 'World of St. Winifred's', the rag of his alma mater. That it was entitled, 'Jesus wants me for a sunbeam', means I must leave you to come to your own conclusions as to his weight and merit as a literary force.

The Bishop

5 March, 2010

Dear Friends

Life at St. Cliff's is destined never to be the same now that my good lady wife has introduced me to the heady delights of 'blogging'.

I am told that this modern form of computerised communication will facilitate a whole new world of interaction via the World Wide Web.

This old dog (and his dog collar – a little bit of humour I am reliably informed will endear me to readers of my missives) has, albeit somewhat reluctantly, removed himself from the cosy warmth of the metaphorical hearth of tradition and entered into this daunting world of instant dialogue.

Rest assured, dear reader of the 'blogosphere', I am not completely green in these matters and have been swotting up on the 'with it' vocabulary of the airwaves.

So, until my next communication, or should I say, 'blog'
... OVER AND OUT!

Onward and upward
Derek

Post Scriptum. It has long been my experience, when preaching to the comatose faithful at St. Cliff's (as the bishop has an unfortunate habit of calling my flock), to feel as if one is broadcasting to thin air. To avoid history being repeated and yours truly 'blogging' to an audience of one man and his proverbial dog, could I prevail on you kind souls of the 'blogosphere' to enlighten fellow 'bloggers' of this humble missive, and perhaps even to encourage them to subscribe to my computerised output? (It is free to one and all I am glad to announce.) Bless you.

Spring has sprung! (Well, almost.)
8 March, 2010

Dear Friends

Not before time am I preparing to bid a fond farewell to the last vestiges of winter. Spring is most definitely in the air at St. Cliff's although, to tell the truth, it's not the only thing.

It would not even require the services of a nasally enhanced bloodhound to detect the disturbing aroma that has recently graced this hallowed building. I was reliably informed that Mrs Bidmarsh and her cleaning ladies had given the pews the 'once over' with Mr Sheen, or some such branded wood reviving agent, in their usual, quick-off-the-mark spring clean (it still being only early March at present). But, as I suspected, what they *intended* to use and what they *actually* ended up coating our ecclesiastical leg rests with, were not one and the same thing.

It was noticeable, last Sunday morning, that the usual high speed evacuation of St. Cliff's sanctuary, which typically follows my 'that's all folks' benediction, appeared to have been supernaturally put on hold. The entire congregation remained firmly seated as if secured to the pews by some unseen hand.

This perceptive diagnosis of mine was not as far off the mark as you might imagine. To everyone's surprise (bar my own – I am well aware of the composite nature of the St. Cliff's Cleaning Committee, being either 100% dotty, blind as a bat or a frightening combination of both), it was not in fact the services of one Mr Sheen that had been employed in this comparatively simple task, but rather those of one Mr SprayFix (patent pending) no less. Whilst displaying himself within the confines of (one has in all fairness to admit) a similarly shaped and coloured receptacle, Mr SprayFix did not confer upon our oaken heirlooms the hoped for result.

Mr Potts, our duty deacon, whose good fortune it was not to have been sitting down, was standing at the back of the church, minding the entrance door against an unlikely invasion from potential gatecrashers, the local criminal underworld, or worse (as far as this doctrinally prejudiced fellow was concerned), charismatics. The next ten minutes were spent persuading him to put to one side his entrenched opinions on Sunday trading and pop down the road to Fags and Mags forthwith to procure, on behalf of the firmly fixed faithful, a dozen tins of lighter fuel which, when applied would hopefully guarantee their freedom.

The departure of Mr Potts was only finally secured and his conscience temporarily salved by reminding him that even Jesus sometimes 'broke the rules' on the Sabbath.

My conscience, on the other hand, still weighs rather heavy having found it necessary to dip into the offering plate to fund this initiative.

Onward and upward

Derek

Bishop visiting St. Cliff's on Sunday. Better not borrow any of his sermon ideas like I did last year when he made an unexpected visit to the church the very day I chose to regurgitate them verbatim. That my talk was entitled "Thou Shall Not Steal" simply compounded my unfortunate gaffe!

Football is biblical!
9 March, 2010

Dear Friends

Oh, what joy it is to read the Bible with the veritable eyes of revelation, and the more so to discover something that has lain hidden from others for two thousand years.

For your information (I am told that letting my guard down and sharing personal details will warm the 'blogging' community to me), I am presently employing a more relaxed method of daily Bible study. This boils down to closing my eyes, opening the Good Book at random, running my finger down the selected page and then beginning my studies from there (having first opened my eyes, of course).

Having had more than my fair share of false starts, which found my index finger drawing my attention to (in no particular order) a rather confusing and contradictory map of the route of the Exodus, the ISBN details and, most frustratingly, the blank page that sits between the Old and New Testaments, it was a joyous surprise and a relief (my run of bad fortune having finally been broken) to find myself faced with the Acts of the Apostles, and chapter 13 in particular.

My joy was increased further when I chanced upon the heading to the page:

'Barnabas and Saul Sent Off'.

That nobody has ever spotted this reference to football in the Bible is astounding. I have come to the conclusion that there is a reason for this revelation being given to me in this year of the football World Cup.

I have made a mental note to write to Mr Kevin Keegan, who, if my memory serves me correctly, is presently the incumbent manager of our 'boys' in the England football team, to share this wonderful discovery with him.

Onward and upward
Derek

All things are possible!
10 March, 2010
Dear Friends

What a blessing my good lady wife is. I am told by those who have their ears to the ground with respect to all things technological that it is possible to launch personal photographs on to the 'blogosphere' (or should that be blogospherical?) airwaves. Not being one such enlightened 'blogger', I have left it to my other half to select and 'post' (I am learning the lingo am I not?) a selection of snaps from my photograph album.

I am simply on tenterhooks with anticipation to know which she will 'upload' first.

Onward and upward
Derek

Derek had always secretly admired the Pope!

Oh, Mother!
11 March, 2010
Dear Friends

Mother's Day fast approaches and I find that my sermon preparation for this annual fixture on the ecclesiastical calendar is laced with more than a little anxiety and much floor pacing.

That this day-long celebration of all things maternal should cast such a long shadow over my normally sanguine demeanour will no doubt surprise you, dear reader. Should not a man of the cloth such as myself exist in a perpetual state of being 'on top of the world', to quote that catchy ditty sung by those paragons of popular music, The Carpenters (who, I gather, no longer grace the popular hit parade as much as one would like)?

In an ideal world the answer to such a searching question would indeed be a hearty affirmative, except for the fact that on this occasion (and on too many others, I confess), I appear to fall foul of sound judgment. I simply cannot seem to help myself in slipping into a default mode of, as the idiom would have it, 'putting my foot in it'.

My impending state of gloom and foreboding with regard to the looming spectre of this year's Mothering Sunday is due in its entirety to my well-intentioned but ill-judged (with hindsight) attempt to capitalise on the renown of that most famous of mums, Mary, the (birth) mother of Jesus, on the occasion of last year's celebration of motherhood.

Had I had the good sense to but enlighten that veritable fount of wisdom (my good lady wife) as to my plans, then the crisis that was wrought would probably have been averted. That I didn't see fit to share my inspired sermon illustration with her prior to its disastrous launch is a decision to be forever rued.

I had cleverly (or so I thought) hit upon the idea of asking the children, on that fated day, to remain (or perhaps more accurately, to be restrained) in the service for an additional five minutes whilst I recounted the story of when Jesus asked his good friend, John, to look after his dear mother from that day hence.

And how better to bring this poignant scene to life than by myself taking the role of Jesus Himself, and employing the services of two of St. Cliff's regulars to play the parts of Mary and John?

What could possibly go wrong?

As the service proceeded I had what can only be described as an epiphany, though please don't tell the bishop. He is a stickler for keeping to the aforementioned church calendar and any such mention of a juxtaposition of epiphany (the festival or otherwise) and Mothering Sunday could be enough to bring about a recurrence of his nervous tick. For the record, it was this unfortunate ailment that put on hold his attendance at the local auction rooms, when one too many twitches of his head unwittingly purchased him job lots of house clearance paraphernalia, also emptying his bank account in the process. But back to my tale.

Placed as if by some divine appointment on the front pew, beneath my very eyes, were none other than the parish's most fearsome of octogenarians, Mrs (Mary) Pilkington-Smythe, and beside her, oblivious to the imminent trauma that was about to be visited upon him, Jonathan Biggins, without doubt the most timid five-year-old you could ever expect to meet.

As an aside, it is my heartfelt suspicion that Mrs Pilkington-Smythe was the inspiration for Roald Dahl's terrifying Miss Trunchbull character, which only compounds my dreadful decision to enlist this real-life Mary and John into my biblical re-enactment.

My next precipitous move down this slippery slope was to quote Jesus' very own words, 'Dear woman, here is your son', with as much Shakespearean gravitas as I could muster.

To everyone's surprise, Mrs Pilkington-Smythe promptly

rose to her feet and embraced the quivering lad as a man-eating octopus (if there is such fanciful creature) might enclose its prey.

The alarm bells ringing in my head should have stopped me in my tracks and caused me to do some sort of audit of the repercussions of this enactment.

They did not.

I was enjoying my moment of thespian glory.

'Son,' I continued, in full Gielgudian flow, 'here is your mother.'

One can only but imagine that the terrified child thought he had been put up for adoption with the ancient battle-axe, which is why to this day, St. Cliff's, as a gesture of remorse (chiefly on my part), is funding his weekly trauma counselling sessions.

Let us hope (and pray) that this Mother's Day is less dramatic, in every sense.

Onward and upward
Derek

Lying low!
15 March, 2010
Dear Friends

I felt compelled to 'log on' to my trusty PC this morning to let you know the outcome of the Mothering Sunday service referred to in my previous missive.

In short, you will be pleased to hear that it passed off without too much tribulation, which is indeed a great relief.

That said, it has taken me more than a little effort this morning to muster up the courage to make outside contact with my fellow participants of the 'blogosphere' for fear of my whereabouts being discovered by the Borough Council Maintenance Department.

How foolish of me to entrust the responsibility of the Mother's

Day gifts (an integral and expected part of St. Cliff's Mother's Day service for fear of summary excommunication by the entrenched matriarchs of the parish) to the youth of the church. In my defence it seemed like a good idea to encourage these oft bored incumbents of the back pew to partake in the life of the church, but perhaps I should have thought twice.

The mums of St. Cliff's were overjoyed to be the recipients of a bunch of spring crocuses but, sad to say, the local council will be less impressed when they next stop by at the village green and discover from whence these flowers came.

I am taking a leaf out of Elijah's book when fleeing from Jezebel, and lying low for a while.

Onward and upward
Derek

Mrs Higginbottom!
20 March, 2010
Dear Friends

Tomorrow I preach on Paul's 'thorn in the flesh' (a thorny topic if ever there was one – a little light humour on my part to cheer you, dear reader) and I feel very much at one with this angst-ridden apostle.

The reason can be put down in its entirety to the fact that I have just cast an uneasy eye over the organ rota for this month, and it is none other than Mrs Higginbottom who appears as the incumbent organist for tomorrow's service.

There are few people who have such an innate ability to mutilate a hymn as the dear lady. I am therefore in a quandary as to whether to affix copious wads of cotton wool into my ear drums to dull the discordant cacophony which is the inevitable result of her fingers gracing (I use this word in the complete opposite sense of that which my Pocket Collins Dictionary describes) the keys of St. Cliff's beast of an organ, or to allow my auditory senses to be assailed by her tuneless and painful assault in an attempt to empathise with Paul's thorny predicament.

Onward and upward

Derek

The age of miracles is not past!
21 March, 2010

Dear Friends

Just when I had given up all hope of a reprieve and was girding my ears for Mrs Higginbottom's 'death by organ', the day was saved in the unexpected guise of fur balls, no less.

Is it so wrong of me to be euphoric that on this of all Sundays, her beloved Tiddles should require the urgent attentions of the 'out of hours' veterinary surgeon to assist in the emergency removal of a stray fur ball? That this coincided with the timing of St. Cliff's morning service (and also her feared residency on the organ) is a miracle indeed.

In the pursuit of honesty, I have to admit that I sent up more than the odd 'arrow' prayer seeking a miraculous deliverance, and am now resigned to spending the rest of this day wrestling with the mixed emotions of guilt (over what I prayed) and elation (that I was spared Mrs Higginbottom's organ playing).

Onward and upward

Derek

Crisis averted!
23 March, 2010
Dear Friends

It is confession time.

Ordinarily I would break from my duties at around eleven of the clock most weekday mornings to partake in a much-needed beverage, namely a mug of warming coffee (Fairtrade, of course) – my 'fix', as my good lady wife prefers to call it, quite unfairly imputing me with some sort of addictive weakness.

This morning, though, I have had to break with this time-honoured and familiar routine, and crack open a box of chocolate liqueurs (it being the only thing of an alcoholic nature that we have under our humble roof, with the exception of twelve boxes of 'swine flu' gel given to me by the bishop for prompt distribution should the parish succumb to that quickly forgotten plague).

The chocolate liqueurs were given to me last Christmas by St. Cliff's Mums and Toddlers' Committee as a reward for entertaining their young charges at the annual Christmas party. The apparent ability of mine to remove my thumb before their very eyes and then to replace it (a mere illusion I would add, should you think I have disturbing, superhuman capabilities), to magically pull a ping pong ball from behind an ear and to juggle three bean bags almost simultaneously, was obviously much appreciated.

The reason that necessitated this emergency intake of intoxicating liquor (though I will not admit to indulging in more than two of the rather scrummy luxury chocolates) was to calm my frayed nerves.

Having spent considerable time in taking a longer-than-average run up before launching myself into the 'blogosphere', I 'logged on' this morning and discovered, to my horror, that a number of my computerised missives had gone A.W.O.L.

It was only after I had engaged the services of 'BlogLine' (an 0800 number thankfully – my meagre stipend, unlike that of the archbishop, not being able to sustain the luxury of using expensive telephonic help lines) – and spoken to a helpful young man (who used far too many references to Great Britain for my liking, as if to prove he was not speaking to me from distant shores) that my bout of the collywobbles was suitably appeased

My errant 'blogs' had been in somewhere called 'Older Posts' at the foot of the page all along.

What was lost has now been found and there is great rejoicing in this household.

Perhaps I can allow myself just one more chocolate liqueur to enhance this present mood of jubilation.

Onward and upward
Derek

Clocks go forward this weekend!
Tempted to put clock on
St. Cliff's bell tower forward not
one but two hours and
then make as if I'm just finishing
the service as everyone arrives.
On second thoughts,
caution must prevail.
Will save pranks until Ist April!

Brain ache!
26 March, 2010

Dear Friends

My mind is presently somewhat addled and I have only but myself to blame for this cranial disorder.

I share this with you en route to partaking of some much-needed medication for this painful condition.

Much against my better nature, and the advice of my good lady wife I will admit, I have been reading up on the rival teachings of Arminianism (the notion that people possess free will to accept or reject salvation) and Calvinism (that God sovereignly chooses those whom He will bring to Himself) in an attempt to impress the theologically stunted of St. Cliffs.

My good lady wife considers it the height of foolishness on my part to overtax an intellect which, to my shame, saw me having to re-sit my Cub Scout Astronomer badge on account of not knowing the difference between the subject in hand and its more dubious cousin, namely astrology.

The net result of this unfortunate error on my part was that I informed our all-too-easily influenced (some would say gullible) Akela, that the present alignment of Ursa Minor and Saturn suggested it was a good time to find himself a wife.

What the young Derek did not know was that his esteemed leader not only had 'another half' already, but that the fruit of this sacred amalgamation was about to break into double figures.

If it had not been for the timely intervention of Baloo (a fervent, born again Christian, who even went so far as to remove the horoscope page from his daily newspaper before his wife had the chance to indulge herself in this 'dangerous dalliance', as he called it), who knows what terrible marital calamity might have ensued? That Akela did not forsake his wife and children in pursuit of pastures new on the basis of my misguided celestial 'heads up', is something for which I will be eternally grateful, and for which Baloo (even to this day I know him as nothing but this childish moniker) must surely take the full credit.

Anyway, here is the conundrum, dear reader.

Into this much-debated doctrinal dispute (forgive me, but a penchant for all things alliterative is a particular weakness of mine) which has polarised the opinions of theologians into these two opposing camps, I am considering the dropping of a pebble in the hope of seeing what ripples it makes.

My rather clever (and somewhat cheeky, though I say it myself) conundrum is this:

Do the supporters of Arminianism have the liberty as to what they believe only because God has sovereignly chosen them to think like that in the first place?

I am calling this 'Calvinistic Arminianism' (patent pending).

And do proponents of Calvinism hold their beliefs in sovereign election only because God has given them freewill to make such a choice?

I am calling this 'Arminian Calvinism' (ditto).

Onward and upward
Derek

Post Scriptum. I fear that this brief foray into the realms of higher theology will rebound on me, and my good lady wife will be proved right. Onward to the medicine cupboard before my head explodes.

A world first!
28 March, 2010
Dear Friends

I believe that I have achieved an all time first.

It is not uncommon (nay, the norm) for a member of St. Cliff's congregation to fall asleep during one of my sermons. This painful slight is something that I have had to come to terms with as 'par for the course'. What is a new experience for me is falling asleep myself in the midst of my own preaching.

I put this squarely down to the lost hour and not to the subject in hand – 'Leviticus Highlights'.

Onward and upward
Derek

A close call indeed!
29 March, 2010
Dear Friends

Confession is good for the soul, or so it is said by someone who obviously knows a thing or two. In an attempt to give this familiar adage additional currency, I must thus gird myself and 'spill the beans' to all and sundry.

The 'Bunyanesque' burden that presently encumbers me is this:

Not only has 'blogging' rather taken over my life of late, the result of which has seen me spending far more time than I would care to admit considering what next to launch on to the 'blogospherical' airwaves (at the cost of my sermon preparation and all things clerical), but I have also (to my shame) had questionable thoughts as to how best to promote myself within this captivating new medium.

Being all too aware that men of the cloth have, in times gone past, strayed into the 'dark side' in the pursuit of filthy lucre and have peddled indulgences for money, I bare my soul to one and all and put my metaphorical hand up to confess to a crime of equal murkiness.

For one mad moment, the offer of 'putting up a prayer' in exchange for the promotion of my 'blog' swam intoxicatingly around my head. The lure of attracting a larger audience than that of a typical Sunday congregation at St. Cliff's (which is not an insurmountable task) was both tantalising and compelling.

Thankfully, I was brought to my senses by an emissary from the good folk at Parcel Force whose persistent hammering on our gargoylic door knocker awoke me from my temporary insanity.

That I had recently purchased over the World Wide Web a copy of 'Graham Kendrick's Greatest Hits' is something for which I will be forever grateful, its noisy delivery being my saving grace.

'Cash for questions' would have had nothing on this had the bishop discovered the error of my ways.

I have made a mental note to meditate on the writings of Solomon that I might be armed with a fresh reserve of wisdom should such a foolish temptation cross my path again.

I will instead rely upon the goodwill of my readers to aid me in the promotion of my 'blog', and thus the growth of my congregation of the airwaves.

Onward and upward
Derek

Must remind Sunday School teachers not to allow their young charges to decorate Easter eggs to look like the bishop as they did last year (at my instigation). I'm still in his bad books for that faux pas though it is hardly my fault he is bald!

My time will come!
30 March, 2010

Dear Friends

How fickle life can be.

My emotions, which I will admit are inclined to veer towards the sensitive at the best of times, have been on what can only be described as a veritable roller coaster ride these past few hours. I am now in a state of feeling supremely let down, like a party balloon that has enjoyed at first fullness, and then its inevitable, ungraceful deflation.

It would have been much better if I had not been the recipient of a letter from the Spring Harvest organising committee, inviting me to be part of the main stage team at Skegness. But, alas, the clock cannot be turned back (unless of course British Summertime is at an end – a little humour to cheer myself at this difficult time).

Perhaps I should have picked up on the fact that it was a tad late in the day to be inviting a main stage speaker to partake of this springtide Christian gathering, but sadly this desperate clergyman did not.

Whilst I would be the first to acknowledge that my preaching at St. Cliff's has not always 'hit the mark', and has not had the same effect as perhaps St. Peter's did on that day of Pentecost when 3,000 were added to the Church, I have always nonetheless held in abeyance the faint hope that I might some day be 'discovered' and elevated to the headier realms of evangelical acclaim.

If I had not had the foresight to show my trophy letter to my good lady wife, I might well have been packing my bags and heading north as we speak to preach to the gathered multitudes.

Instead, I have been saved the humiliation of being removed from the Spring Harvest main stage as an interloper by her timely discovery that the 'ministry opportunity' I was being offered was in fact for stacking the platform chairs at the end of each session.

I am now resolved to give my very best to my faithful (yet significantly smaller) flock at St. Cliff's this coming Sunday in the hope that my time will come.

I have also decided to pass up the generous opportunity to work with chairs that has been offered to me.

Onward and upward
Derek

Derek got the idea from a lorry he was following!

Emergency!
31 March, 2010
Dear Friends

My apologies that I have scant time to communicate with my 'online' congregation on this rain-soaked day. A pastoral emergency has laid claim to my time.

It being Wednesday, the local tradesmen (for some reason that no doubt harks back to I know not when) deem it acceptable to withdraw their labour for the duration of the afternoon of this particular day each week, and thus all businesses within the parish (with the exception of Fags and Mags which appears not to possess a 'Closed' sign) remain firmly shut.

This includes the local veterinary practice and I have therefore been called upon to lay hands on Mr Piddlington's pet tortoise in the hope that a speedy recovery will ensue.

I have not had time to scour my Bible to discover whether or not the exercise I am about to embark on is biblical or otherwise. I surmise that the results will tell all, and should my endeavours not 'do the trick', as Mr Piddlington put it, let us at least pray that the inert creature makes it through to the morning, when the veterinary surgery's presently withdrawn expertise becomes available once more.

Onward and upward

Derek

pagan rituals and thus we will not be inviting the Morris men to perform at St Cliff's Summer Fair.

It has been decided that St Cliff's recent purchase of inflatable kneelers will be returned to the supplier immediately. Whilst this cost-cutting exercise was considered to be expedient at the time the subsequent embarrassment to users caused by the noisy expulsion of air through faulty valves, often at inappropriate times during our services, has forced our hand.

On Wednesday at 8pm St Cliff's Gardening Society will be presenting an evening entitled 'Love Thy Neighbour...But Not Their Leylandii'

There's no fool …

1 April, 2010

Dear Friends

April, that month of fools, is indeed upon us, and my one and only attempt at giving in to the irresistible urge to see a fellow human being come a cropper as they succumb to some childish prank or other has not resulted in the hoped for outcome I would have anticipated.

Whilst I would not wish to make too strong a link between myself and St. John (and his Patmosian revelation), it would not be too far off the mark to suggest that the idea that somewhat impishly popped into my head, during the final stages of setting the communion table, was a wondrous inspiration indeed.

The first day of April, Maundy Thursday service and old Mrs Higginbottom's name on the organ roster are probably as rare a convergence as any solar eclipse and, in that respect, far too good an opportunity to pass up.

In but a trice, an ample quantity of superfluous communion wafers were whisked away for summary re-housing within the darkened depths of St. Cliff's trusty old pipe organ to await a terrifyingly discordant and turbulent fate.

Pride, as they say, comes before a fall, and the smug expression that was working its way unstoppably across my face in eager expectation of the fruitful culmination of my mischievous master plan was, unbeknownst to me, already packing its bags and preparing to leave.

My downfall lay squarely in my fateful choice of first hymn. Whilst 'Guide me O thou Great Jehovah' is as good a stirring anthem as any to get the circulation flowing through the veins of St. Cliff's comatose faithful, its hearty refrain could not have been employed on much worse a day.

Such bad timing as you could ever have wished for was only compounded by the very first usage of the wafer-stuffed pipes coinciding in unfortunate synchronicity with the singing of the lines, 'Bread of heaven'.

The raucous cacophony of Mrs Higginbottom's failed attempt to do this old favourite justice was only outdone by the ensuing stampede as the congregation, en masse, thrust forward to catch the apparent miraculous supply of manna that cascaded earthward.

My futile efforts to come clean and to put the record straight that I was to blame for this 'miracle' were simply seen as unbelief on my part and not worthy of someone of my calling.

To make matters worse (if that were at all possible), some bright spark suggested that we should forsake our suppers and instead wait upon the Lord for a complementary supply of quail to be visited upon us.

We would probably still be sitting there waiting with unabated hunger, had not Mrs Higginbottom seen fit to pass the time by inflicting upon the captive audience her reminiscent-of-Les-Dawson (a comedic English entertainer who had a talent for playing the pianoforte rather badly, for those not from these shores) version of 'The Entertainer'. Her painful rendition had the effect of dislodging a lagging communion wafer, thus revealing my folly and saving our ears from the ravages of death by organ recital.

Such was the gratitude of the congregation for their timely salvation from the latter that they were more than magnanimous in letting me off the hook, just this once.

Onward and upward
Derek

Creme Egg catastrophe!

4 April, 2010

Dear Friends

How wonderful on this Easter day to acknowledge God's abundant goodness to one and all.

I cannot help but wonder at the splendid miracle that takes mere mortals like you and me and transforms us into His perfect likeness.

That this 'mere mortal' is perhaps feeling a little more in need of God's forgiveness than others on this particular day can be put down squarely to my mistakenly indulging in the Cadbury's Creme Egg that was placed temptingly in the church vestry this morning.

The fact that this was a 'thank you' gift from St. Cliff's children to our gap year children's worker (and not to yours truly) was a mistake that has cost me dear.

Not only did a greater proportion of the egg decide to settle on my dog collar than in my salivating mouth (and thus cause me great embarrassment and discomfort for the duration of the Easter service), but I now have to salve my conscience from the impulsive and desperate fib that I told to the children to appease their tears, that the church cleaner had probably taken the Creme Egg by mistake.

I find myself here wrestling with the opportunity to avail myself of God's complete forgiveness (on which I preached with such faith this very morning) or ceding to the flesh and embracing a self-imposed penance of abstaining from chocolate throughout this Easter period, in the hope that perhaps this alternative course of action will aid my deliverance from this presently all-consuming guilt.

Onward and upward

Derek

Post Scriptum. My mind is made up. It is, as modern parlance would have it, a 'no brainer'. I will assuredly opt for the former choice. It would seem that my preaching does indeed 'deliver the goods' after all.

A dilemma indeed!
9 April, 2010
Dear Friends

A most embarrassing and awkward situation has cropped up and it is one that is causing me much concern.

I have, of late, been encouraged by the bishop to broaden my horizons pertaining to things theological and doctrinal (with regard to my choice of reading matter), and to move out of my 'comfort zone'.

He assures me that such a move will enable me to engage more readily with the common man (or, I hasten to add for fear of sending ripples across the already choppy waters of feminism – woman) in my preaching.

I would surmise that his rationale is that word is out that I have not received a single nomination for the much esteemed 'World of Anglicanism Sermon of the Year 2009' competition. Despite the slightly hurtful undertones of the bishop's well-meaning suggestion, I have nonetheless decided to embrace his advice and to join the local library forthwith.

It is many a year since I last availed myself of the opportunity to borrow from the municipal literature pool and, much to my surprise, I discover that I now need to supply not just my name and address but also photographic identification (or 'ID' as I believe it is called in the modern vernacular).

I found myself having to leave my completed (but not yet approved) application form with the rather surly librarian on the ill-named 'Customer Care' desk, and 'hot foot it' to the nearby

Boots the Chemist outlet, where (I was brusquely informed) they had a photographic booth for just such occurrences as these.

Having spent a good ten minutes falteringly attempting to familiarise myself with the requirements of the said photographic booth, I pulled back the curtain and positioned myself purposefully for the off.

The unfortunate sequence of events that followed are those to which I referred at the outset of this missive.

Having mentally rehearsed the four poses that I wished to assume for the automated photographer, I deposited the requisite coins in the machine and waited with my first frozen pose.

As the initial dazzling flash illuminated the cramped cubicle, and all but blinded me, a voice addressed me from the other side of the closed curtain.

The voice was not, it seemed, intent on engaging in conversation but rather in unburdening their weighted soul of its unsavoury contents.

This untimely interruption temporarily fazed my normally calm clerical demeanour, causing me to produce poses for the impatient camera that were nothing like those I had planned.

In a matter of seconds I had been captured for posterity sporting a variety of facial expressions that ranged from bewilderment to consternation.

It would appear that the poor (and somewhat misguided) person outside of the cubicle had observed my ministerial entrance and mistakenly thought it to be some sort of mobile confessional booth.

Not only did my photographs suffer the effects of this unwarranted disturbance, but I am now uncertain as to what to do with the supposedly confidential information my 'confessee' inadvertently passed my way.

I think I can overlook the small matter of his pretending to gift a busker with a pound coin when in fact it was a half melted, out-of-date chocolate version. However, his admittance that he has a stash of unreturned library books at home numbering into the hundreds is of a completely different order.

I now found myself in somewhat of a dilemma.

If I return to the library to complete my application, is it my public duty to report the deluded fellow's literary light-fingeredness or should I remain tight-lipped and retain the integrity of the confessional (photographic or otherwise)?

Not only that, but my dilemma is laced with irony in that I am sure there is a jolly useful tome in print that tackles all such ecclesiastical quandaries. But there are no prizes for guessing from which particular municipal facility I would have to borrow it.

Onward and upward

Derek

Derek's worst nightmare
— a hugger!

A veritable inspiration!
15 April, 2010
Dear Friends

It is now some months since I was confronted in the vestibule of St. Cliff's by young Billy Butlin (his parents having enjoyed many a windswept break at his namesake's once popular coastal establishments), and asked in a surprisingly forthright manner (for one so young) if Santa Claus was real or not.

It soon became clear to one and all (it was unfortunate that a crowd of my exiting congregation had decided to make it their business to discover the nature of my reply) that this plucky lad was not going to be palmed off with a fudged response.

While he waited, hands on hips, for my ministerial wisdom to be dispensed, I could not help but think of Solomon when he was presented with one baby and two contenders for its mother.

If I answered in the affirmative to young Billy's provocative question then I could quite rightly be accused of lying. If, on the other hand, I stated that I did not believe that Santa Claus existed (or Father Christmas, as some of us still prefer to know this fabled bringer of gifts), then I would no doubt risk the accusation by both parents and congregation alike of being a spoilsport and ruining the lad's childhood.

In a moment of inspiration, I shelved my thoughts of Solomon and settled on Jesus' approach to the Pharisees when he confronted their vehement accusations to a woman caught in adultery. I courageously decided that it was time to play my 'if anyone is without sin' trump card, and turned this somewhat tense situation on its head by throwing the question open to 'the floor'.

When confronted by this challenging festive conundrum, the menacing crowd of onlookers swiftly slunk away (to my relief I must add).

This close call has set my mind racing. If a crisis of the like that

I have just described can be averted by the delivery of incisive wisdom (forgive me if perhaps I blow my own trumpet a tad too loudly), then why not offer my services to the wider world?

It is to this end that I am throwing open to all-comers the invitation to ask of me whatever theological or biblical questions they may have, and I will do my utmost to present them with my considered response.

There is absolutely no stopping me in this and I have taken the liberty of 'setting up' a Hotmail account with which to receive your puzzled communications.

Your questions can be submitted to me at (or should I say '@' to prove that I am no Luddite in matters technological) **askderekthecleric@hotmail.co.uk**

I will be calling this feature, 'Ask Derek', although I should add, for fear of getting swamped and thus being unable to fulfil my clerical duties (and incurring the wrath of the bishop), that I will not be able to answer every question, simply those that I consider worthy of a response.

I will make a point of checking my 'inbox' on regular occasions to see what interesting questions have been posed.

I await expectantly.

Onward and upward
Derek

In response to my new feature, 'Ask Derek', in which I offer to employ my experience and wisdom (such as it is) to answer church-related or theological conundrums, Stephen Lucas from England asks ...

Derek,
You are a legend! Full of wisdom.
Church PA is a fascination of mine.
How do you get on with your PA (audio) volunteers at St. Cliff's? And how do they get on with your congregation/musicians?!

Dear Sir

Thank you for your kind words and for your pertinent question.

I will readily admit that those entrusted with the weekly task of performing the technical equivalent of CPR on our somewhat antiquated public address system at St. Cliff's are rather a law unto themselves. Whilst they may be located at the rear of the church, away from the gaze of the congregation, I am not the only one to have noted that, once seated proudly behind the 'sound desk', they very much consider themselves the *de facto* captains of the ship.

Having seen fit, on occasions, not only to remove from our worship team the necessary amplification with which to drown out the accompaniment of our less-then-melodious organist, Mrs Higginbottom, (patently preferring a more traditional approach to church music) these custodians of the volume control have also, on occasion, denied yours truly the benefit of the voice-enhancing technology at their fingertips when my theology did not apparently square with theirs.

But then I hit upon a cunning ruse to curtail this scurrilous sound desk insubordination once and for all. Realising that there was nothing that irritates a PA operative more than for a preacher to ask, 'Is it on?' (when referring to the microphone), I therefore resolved to use this line mercilessly until they eventually capitulated. These three little words have the net effect of challenging their technical competence before the assembled throng, the most heinous of crimes in the world of audio 'geekery'.

You will be pleased to hear that my victory was swift and enduring and, once more, this humble clergyman is at the helm.

Should a further mutiny rear its ugly head at some time hence, I will have no qualms about using my other weapon – that of suggesting the congregation proffer feedback on how well these servants of the sound system are doing their job.

I have it on good authority that, above all others, 'feedback' is one word that no PA operative ever wants to hear.

Onward and upward
Derek

...e sincerely hope that next time the communion wine will not be corked.

Last week's report from the deliverance ministry training day stated that, 'during the personal ministry time there was a bit of a pavlova'.

This should have read, 'a bit of a palaver'.

'I know my plaice'.

A fishmonger's wife tells of her call to the Anglican ministry.

This Thursday at 7.30pm.

That really takes the biscuit!
19 April, 2010
Dear Friends

Having run out of chocolate digestives (a particular indulgence of mine) and with 'elevenses' looming large, I took it upon myself to take our faithful (though somewhat temperamental) Nissan Micra on the short journey to the Co-operative Society's local outlet to replenish my stocks of the said biscuity snack.

I will be the first to raise a guilty hand and admit that it would have been far better for both the environment and for my health to have walked, but I did not. My excuse (feeble though it may appear) was that I was in mid flow with my preparations for a talk to the Parish Boxing Club (my being their newest incumbent in the role of chaplain), who had invited me to round off their annual awards dinner with a short epilogue. I had immediately hit upon (forgive the pun, I simply cannot seem to help myself sometimes) a light-hearted look at pugilists from the Bible and I was eager not to lose my train of thought.

Shamefully shelving all thoughts of my carbon footprint, I parked up and entered the grocery establishment to purchase a packet of their own brand chocolate digestives, they being of equal quality with the market leader yet not breaking the bank of this hardly overly-recompensed clergyman.

Had I not been waylaid by Mrs McTavish, a parishioner of mine who was insistent that I 'break with tradition' and try a wee tin of Scottish shortbread for a change, then the outcome of this excursion might have been happier.

That she had me cornered for the best part of half an hour in the interests of converting me to her suggested variety of biscuit meant that on exiting the shop, I discovered that my abandoned car had attracted a parking ticket for overstaying its welcome by some thirty seconds (a half hour being the apportioned limit).

To make matters worse, the conferrer of this automotive penalty (a rather self-satisfied traffic warden) I recognised as being the treasurer of the United Reformed Church within the town.

It did not take me long to 'join the dots' as they say and to work out why the delivery of my parking ticket seemed to be causing him such pleasure. I attribute his vindictive (though, I hasten to add, lawful) action down to the fact that two members of his congregation had recently defected to St. Cliff's, bringing with them their ample tithe.

That this decision was swayed by their attendance (of their own accord I might add) at the seasonally popular 'Carols at St. Cliff's', and that they preferred our choice of tune for 'O little town of Bethlehem' to the 'unchristmassy' version that the URC minstrels chose to serve up, is something that was entirely out of my control (but obviously not as far as a particular officious traffic warden was concerned).

Whilst it is tempting to take, in lieu of payment, a lesson or two in the art of boxing from my new 'fisticuff fellowship' in order to confront the patently ticked-off treasurer, I fear that turning the other cheek will have to be the order of the day.

As a result of this morning's untimely events, 'elevenses' is now 'twelveses'. I will do my best to comfort myself with not one but two of Mrs McTavish's heavily promoted biscuit alternatives in the hope that I can get back on track with my talk.

Onward and upward
Derek

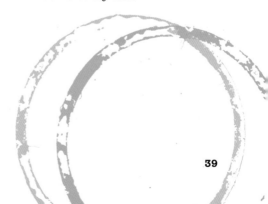

Fame at last!
21 April, 2010

It is now some years since I received plaudits for my prize-winning entry in the ever popular St. Winifred's Annual Charity Week Caption Competition (St. Winifred's being my alma mater). The acclaim, of which I received much, still gladdens my heart to this day. To that end I thought it fitting to include it in this tome dedicated to my good self for your delectation and pleasure.

ED'S CHARITY WEEK MAGAZINE

CAPTION COMPETITION

"DON'T WORRY SIR, MY SURGICAL HEALING MINISTRY IS QUITE SCRIPTURAL"

The winner in our competition was Derek, a first year student at St Winifred's, with his witty caption to this picture from the new PG rated (and thus suitable for students at this establishment) blockbuster film, Indiana Jones and the Temple of Doom.

Blacklisted!
24 April, 2010
Dear Friends

How wonderful indeed it has been of late to enjoy such an extended period of springtide sunshine (albeit laced with a little more volcanic ash than one would have perhaps liked).

With summer assuredly on the horizon, I dusted off my trusty bathing costume in preparation for an outing to the local swimming baths. In the interests of personal hygiene (and out of consideration for my fellow bathers), I decided that it would be advisable to pay a precautionary visit to my GP to review the recurrent outbreak of verrucas that plague the soles of my feet as ferociously as those plagues which afflicted the land of Egypt in Moses' day.

Attempting to obtain an appointment with the rather unfortunately named Doctor Crippen (no relation I am glad to say), proved to be a task more difficult than I had imagined. It transpired that each time I succeeded in getting through to the fearsome receptionist who jealously guards the surgery from intruders (aka sick people), I was palmed off with the same excuse: 'We are sorry, Reverend, but the doctor is fully booked.'

I did not believe for one deluded moment that there was even a hint of genuine regret in this continual series of telephonic letdowns, nor that the doctor in question was so over-worked that he could not squeeze in a fellow public servant for a minor medical examination such as mine would undoubtedly have been.

If it had not been for a little bird elucidating this baffled clergyman with respect to this frustrating episode, then I would have remained 'in the dark' as to the true nature of my inability to get an appointment.

Due to a combination of hypochondria, an unfortunate weak bladder and an innate ability to attract the attention of just about every passing sickness, this 'little bird' (otherwise known as Mrs Sturgeon, she who has been typing up St. Cliff's Weekly News Sheet since the days of Noah) had found herself spending almost every waking hour in the aforementioned doctor's surgery, and was thus privy to the inmost secrets of the place, including my predicament.

That our 100% 'hit rate' in last Sunday evening's healing service wiped out (by an amazing coincidence) all of the doctor's patients for the following day in one fell swoop, and earned him an immediate reprimand from his PCT for not meeting his targets, is hardly my fault.

Whether it is acceptable, within the boundaries of the law of this land, to 'blacklist' a patient (such as myself) for 'poaching' (as Doctor Crippen has accused me of) is debatable.

I must comfort myself with the fact that such ointments and embrocations as are necessary to resolve my pedal infirmity will have to be purchased from the pharmaceutical chemist, and trust that this self-administered treatment will keep the irritating ailment at bay.

Doctor Crippen's wife occasionally shows her face at St. Cliff's, which will present me with an opportunity for grace, particularly if she turns up the next time we lay hands on the sick. I have resolved that this is one public servant who won't be unavailable, especially as it is common knowledge that the lady is afflicted by the very same condition for which her entrenched husband has withheld treatment from this foot-sore clergyman.

Onward and upward
Derek

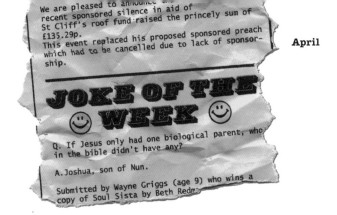

We are pleased to announce ...
recent sponsored silence in aid of
St Cliff's roof fund raised the princely sum of
£135.29p.
This event replaced his proposed sponsored preach
which had to be cancelled due to lack of sponsor-
ship.

JOKE OF THE WEEK 😊 😊

Q. If Jesus only had one biological parent, who
in the bible didn't have any?

A. Joshua, son of Nun.

Submitted by Wayne Griggs (age 9) who wins a
copy of Soul Sista by Beth Redm~

An offer that I perhaps *could* refuse!

30 April, 2010

Dear Friends

If there is one pastime for which I have a particular penchant, it is that of rambling.

The 'great outdoors' is medicine indeed after the sometimes claustrophobic confines of St. Cliff's, and I find this leisure pursuit a most therapeutic exercise.

Therefore to receive an invitation to be chaplain of the local rambling society was a most harmonious proposition, a perfect juxtaposition of both work and pleasure.

I now feel a tad uneasy, having been subsequently informed by the committee chairman of the said society that their rationale for suggesting yours truly for this esteemed position was that they considered my sermon style and their leisure pursuit to have much in common!

What they mean by that I am unclear, but I think I will 'put on hold' their proposal while I ponder the inference of this somewhat disconcerting statement.

Onward and upward
Derek

What are the odds of that happening?
3 May, 2010

Dear Friends

It is good to attempt to get into the proverbial boots of a biblical character and, for me, Adam is someone with whom I am presently able to empathise. To have the richness of Eden paraded before his very eyes only to have it whipped from under his nose (albeit because of some rather ill-advised scrumping) would seem to be a terrible fate indeed.

As you will be well aware if you are a regular at St. Cliff's (and in this I do not include Mr and Mrs Duckworth who are only regular by default of their prolific production of little Duckworths and thus their consequent christenings), I do not fight shy of flying in the face of popular opinion where biblical standards are concerned.

That said, my timing could not have been worse when I took it upon myself on Sunday to tackle, headlong, both the National Lottery and its obvious bedfellow, the thorny issue of sanctified giving.

Having put to one side the all-pervasive thoughts of St. Cliff's Roof Fund, which presently seems to consume my every waking (and often as not, sleeping) hour, I valiantly launched forth into the evils of gambling and the demerits of attempting to 'launder' ill-gotten gains so as to make them somehow acceptable to God.

I doubt whether even a betting man could have proffered odds for such an unlikely event as Mr Smithers (the recent recipient of a rather sizeable lottery cheque) choosing yesterday of all unfortunate days to tithe his winnings to St. Cliff's.

As a result of my unambiguous sermon, not only was I unable to secure a goodbye handshake from our much-maligned and none-too-happy potential donor (in a bid to keep the lines of communication at least partially intact), I then unwittingly added insult to injury by foolishly attempting to make light of the whole thing and joking that we were happy to take money from just about anybody when it came to the Roof Fund ... even bankers. Chortle, chortle.

It was only as Mr Smithers put himself somewhat aggressively into fifth gear and accelerated down the length of the church path, with much huffing and puffing, that my flustered head chose to remind me how indeed the offended fellow earned his living.

In the light of these unfortunate happenings and the loss of this financial gift to St. Cliff's coffers, I have made a mental note to preach on forgiveness next Sunday.

Let us hope that the Roof Fund Committee are all in attendance or I may well find myself empathising with Daniel and his episode with the lions also.

Onward and upward
Derek

A not so sound idea!
13 May, 2010
Dear Friends

Here at St. Cliff's we know very little of the march of progress, rather more a slow amble by which even a snail would not be much challenged.

That said, this is not for the want of trying on my part and to that end, I take great pride in having recently circumnavigated the latent Luddite tendencies inherent within my congregation by facilitating the installation of a sound system within our ancient walls.

Pride, as they say, comes before a fall and, whilst I have yet to experience a toppling of the kind promised by this familiar adage, I fear that it is now only a matter of time before I taste its culmination.

Had I but spent as much time selecting the 'PA team' (I believe that this is the correct collective terminology) as I had poring over the enticing brochures that purveyed the technological wizardry proffered, then the situation that has now arisen could have been avoided.

That Mr Higginbottom should volunteer his services to be part of this team was, in truth, a disaster in the making, and for that I only have myself to blame.

Being the 'other half' of Mrs Higginbottom, our longest serving (and cacophonous) organist, has left the poor man with not only permanently impaired hearing but also rather fixed views about what type of instruments should be used in church. Anything that can be strummed, hit with sticks or enhanced with microphones is simply not worthy of consideration in his extremely conservative book.

To now find Mr Higginbottom on the trial rota for operating our new auditory acquisition has proved somewhat awkward to say the least.

As if it is not enough for the fellow to 'twiddle the knobs' (in a downward direction) to such a degree that we might as well not have plundered the last dregs of St. Cliff's Emergency Fund to secure such a forward-thinking technological purchase, he also considers it within his remit to remove every last vestige of sound-enhancing advantage from any person of the fairer sex who partakes in our services (in support of his similarly entrenched views about women speaking in church).

I have cunningly hit upon an idea of how to relieve the awkward man of his responsibilities so that normal service may be satisfactorily resumed as quickly as possible. However, between you and me, it has left me feeling more than a tad uncomfortable.

My plan is to enlist the support of Mr Higginbottom's fellow operatives (who are very much on my side in this respect) in a bid to remove him from his position of power. Whilst in my heart I believe that it is for the greater good of St. Cliff's that he goes (post-haste), I am uneasy about my proposal that we meet together with the pretence of praying about who should remain on the team but all along agreeing amongst ourselves as to the outcome; the ousting of this difficult fellow.

I fear that I have a great deal more wrestling with my conscience to do before I reach a satisfactory conclusion.

It most certainly has no intention of quietening down any time soon!

Onward and upward
Derek

I am star struck!
13 May, 2010
Dear Friends

I have just returned from a brief foray onto my World Wide Web Facebook portal (I am like a child on Christmas morning – I simply cannot seem to resist 'logging on' to see if I have yet another new companion on the social networking airwaves), and I am all a-flutter with excitement from the discovery that I now have in excess of two hundred 'friends'.

Whilst I recognise that for some this would not be classed as a momentous occasion, for this particular clergyman a congregation of that size (for indeed that is what they are to me) is a veritable answer to my prayers.

If it had not been for the eagle eyes of my good lady wife, I would have been none the wiser as to the composite nature of my 'online' flock. It was she who, glancing over my shoulder as she passed by (no doubt checking to see that I had not succumbed to yet another internet scam, following my close shave with a kindly gentleman from Nigeria with whom I had struck up a friendship after being informed by him that he was presently a little down on his luck and could do with borrowing some cash to tide him over), noticed that I appeared to have more than a few 'celebrities' claiming allegiance to yours truly.

It is all I can do to keep a level head and not become a tad star struck at the very thought of it!

Certainly God is not a respecter of persons and I, likewise, must assuredly treat every person with similar equity. That, as they say, is easier said than done.

Since that oft remembered day when I secured the autograph of Mr Cliff Richard, no less, on my copy of his chart-topping gramophone recording, 'Mistletoe and Wine' (a particular favourite of mine, I confess), I simply cannot seem to resist the allure of celebrity.

Being one who is more accustomed to making friends in the traditional environment of the ubiquitous church social, I am a little unsure as to the strength of my new found friendships on this well known internet portal, and to what degree I can presume upon their loyalty.

With summer fast approaching and St. Cliff's Summer Fete Committee convening next week, it is all I can do to hold at bay thoughts of throwing caution to the wind and inviting one of the aforementioned celebrities to grace us with their presence.

I will admit that, since last year's Methodist circuit Summer Fair was opened by a tone deaf young lad (as far as I could make out from the excessively amplified, strained vocal that wafted across the drizzly skies to assault our ears) who had appeared briefly on a television programme entitled the *X Factor* (but had not furthered his ambitions as a result), I have been attempting to valiantly trump their efforts.

Whilst recognising that this is probably not completely adhering to the ecumenical spirit that we, the churches of the town, have committed to foster, I have temporarily appeased my conscience with the thought that by flinging wide the gates of St. Cliff's to folk from all denominations, they will also be able to benefit from the efficacy of rubbing shoulders with the celebrities who have chosen to endorse me, if I can be so bold as to put it that way.

That my ultimate rationale for doing this is that it will give me additional kudos on the ministers' fraternal is but a niggling thought that I will endeavour to silence.

But then again, perhaps all things considered, I would do well to broach this matter first with the Summer Fete Committee prior to any approaches that I might wish to make. I am led to believe that celebrities do indeed make a small charge for such appearances and it might well be that a £10 book token is simply not enough to secure their attendance.

Onward and upward
Derek

Two birds with one stone!
16 May, 2010
Dear Friends

The matter is resolved!

Mr Higginbottom, the rather awkward gentleman I referred to in a previous missive, is no longer with us. Not in the 'six feet under' sense (though I will admit to wishing him so on more than one occasion), but rather, I have secured his removal from St. Cliff's fledgling PA team.

Fortunately I came to my senses and did not implement the shameful and shady charade (my alliterative gift is simply irrepressible) that I had been considering, but rather I employed a far more effective (if not a little canny) strategy to elicit the desired result.

Having just enjoyed an episode of Mr Patrick Moore's televisual treat, *The Sky at Night*, which featured the alignment of the planets, I hit upon the idea of bringing together a convergence of the like that even the most seasoned star gazer would appreciate.

This Sunday I ensured that both Mr and Mrs Higginbottom were on the rota for St. Cliff's morning service – Mrs Higginbottom perched behind the clavinova (borrowed for the occasion, our pipe organ being temporarily out of action and in need of repair, no doubt due in the main to Mrs Higginbottom's unrestrained thumping of the ancient instrument), and Mr Higginbottom behind the sound desk 'twiddling the knobs'.

The fact that Mrs Higginbottom could not be heard (because Mr Higginbottom had 'zeroed' the sound level of this 'modern and unsuitable' instrument) was an obvious blessing to us all, although it has not done a great deal to enrich their marriage. While they both take a little time out to resolve their differences, I have suggested that perhaps it would be wise to remove themselves from the Sunday rota.

And that, dear friends, is most definitely music to my ears!

Onward and upward
Derek

and regulars at St Cliff's will be pleased to hear that our prayer ministry team 'catchers' (for those slain in the Spirit) will in future be operating under a far more robust code of conduct.
"Oops, butter fingers!" will no longer be an acceptable excuse for dropping clientele.

We would like to apologise for any inferred intellectual superiority during the course of last Sunday's reading from the book of Acts and the account of Peter addressing the post-Pentecost crowd.
To put the record straight Peter was in fact referring to Cretans and not cretins as was unfortunately stated.

FOR SALE

Complete set of St Cliff's 2010 sermon tapes. Unused

A predicament!
19 May, 2010
Dear Friends

I am in a bit of a predicament.

Last evening was the first meeting of our new Alpha course at St. Cliff's, and seven souls (as yet unredeemed one assumes) assembled to journey together on Mr Gumbel's wonderful, food-enhanced exploration of the Christian message.

Whilst an 'ice-breaker' component was not featured within the helpful notes supplied, I simply felt unable to resist beginning the evening with one of my favourite party games – namely, 'Passing the Orange Under the Chin'.

Being somewhat preoccupied with a rather enticing phone call from a gentleman offering me (and one other) a free holiday in exchange for just an hour or so of my time on Saturday somewhere in Central London, I dispatched my good lady wife to purchase an ample supply of oranges from our local greengrocer.

Reg's Veg and Fruit (originally referred to without the fruit component in its title, until the proprietor realised that, whilst the word play pertaining to his name might have been mildly amusing, it had the net effect of withholding from the casual passer-by the full potential of his wares) was the purveyor of oranges of such a bright hue that it was difficult to imagine that even nature (and by that I mean God) could create such a vividly coloured delicacy as that which met my wife's bedazzled eyes.

There was more truth to my surmising than you might imagine.

The enterprising (and slightly dishonest) greengrocer, on taking delivery of the oranges in question, considered that they were a tad under-ripe for his liking (and that of his picky clientele) and had thus given the green-tinged fruit the quick 'once over' with a can of orange automobile paint which he had

Derek knows how to guarantee a good turn out!

to hand for the use of touching up his battered (and tastelessly orange) delivery vehicle.

That this additional coating to the 'doctored' fruit chose to remove itself onto the sweaty chins (and clothing) of my Alpha attendees at the onset of the amusing party game scuppered St. Cliff's hopes of upping our membership numbers (by seven to be precise) in an instant.

Resisting my attempts to remove the offending paint from their persons with turpentine and an abrasive scourer borrowed from the church kitchen (and which will need replacing before the terrifying matriarchs who rule that domain discover its disappearance), they exited the church, en masse, vowing never to set foot in the place ever again.

As a mark of protest I have instructed my good lady wife that from now, and until further notice, we will be reneging on our commitment to 'buy local' and will forthwith purchase our fruit and vegetables from the popular out-of-town supermarket.

I safely predict that the good folk at Alpha will not be tapping us up any time soon for a 'success story' to grace the pages of their promotional newspaper.

Onward and upward
Derek

It's the way I tell 'em!
22 May, 2010
Dear Friends

Last Sunday at St. Cliff's, whilst endeavouring to lighten the leaden atmosphere after Colonel Pettigrew's unfortunate attempt to bring a prophetic word during the morning service, I discovered a gift that until then I had been blissfully unaware that I possessed.

It was the ability to render a joke in public.

The occasion of this surprising revelation was instigated by Colonel Pettigrew's unexpected appearance on the platform at the front of the church.

This was all the more shocking as the fellow had never previously even opened his moustache-topped mouth in a service, let alone 'let rip' in the manner that he did, which would have had even Jeremiah the prophet quaking in his boots.

Calling down heaven's entire reserves of fire and brimstone, he vehemently laid the accusation that there was one among us who had 'fallen from grace'.

It was not until the conclusion of the service that we discovered that St. Cliff's hearing loop had chosen that fated moment to play up, and instead of my dulcet tones reverberating in his earpiece, the perturbed Colonel had 'picked up' what he erroneously believed to be the voice of God giving him inside information pertaining to 'sin in the camp'. It was in fact little more than a phone-in on a popular wireless station where a gentleman was, it appears, in the flow of spilling the beans on his errant wife.

While Ms Slight, our rather burly (and ill-named) duty deacon, manhandled Colonel Pettigrew back to his pew (perhaps with a little more force than was required, St. Cliff's not being 'B' Wing of the local Category A prison where she serves as a prison officer the rest of the time), I attempted to draw the attention of the congregation away from the fracas by deciding that a dose of humour might be just what was required.

For the life of me I could not remember a single joke, but what did spring to mind was that time-honoured conundrum enquired of in school playgrounds up and down this fair land:

'Why did the chicken cross the road?'

In a moment of reckless inspiration (and no doubt because I had been reading from the Gospel of Luke, chapter 10, verses 25–37 whilst I partook of my daily bowl of Kellogg's All-Bran that very morning), I surprised even myself by also blurting out the following answer:

'That is not the question but rather, what on earth was the chicken doing in the story of the Good Samaritan in the first place?'

I will admit that my humour may be a little too clever for some. I did after all notice that there were few smiles returned in recognition of my witty repartee, but I trust that with time the penny will drop and the joke will be 'got'.

I simply cannot wait until I have another gem of this calibre to share with you.

In the interim, I will also make a mental note to have our hearing loop looked at. With my sermon on hearing God's still, small voice looming large, I can ill afford a repeat performance!

Onward and upward
Derek

...and to apologise that last week's Pet Sunday service coincided with a sermon in the ongoing 'Leviticus Highlights' series entitled 'Animal Sacrifices Made Easy'.

Congratulations to the bishop on winning first prize in the town carnival fancy dress competition.

Unfortunately this was the result of an embarrassing mix up in that whilst the bishop had been invited along to bless the event his appearance in a cassock was mistaken by the organisers of the aforementioned competition for a costumed entry into their somewhat controversial 'Drag' category.

STOP PRESS

We would like to dispel the rumour that St Cliff's new ladies weight-watching group is to be called The Woman of Some Area.

last Sunday's much advertised sermon on tithing will be preached for a second time due to an unusually poor attendance.

Next weekend St Cliff's hosts the Mighty Women of God conference which is designed to help the ladies of our church rise up to be everything to which God has called them.
We will be looking at the lives of Deborah, Ruth and Esther and what they can teach us about not being held back by social stereotypes.

Souvenir aprons and tea towels will be available to buy at the event.

We apologise for the misprint in last week's news sheet. This Thurday's talk at the Men's Supper Club by Mr Stobbs about his life ...ter Board should have in... and not

St Cliff's

THE BEST CHURCH IN TOWN!

Ecumenism was never one of Derek's strengths!

BOARD

The seminar 'Borrowing Money Without Getting Into Debt' has been cancelled due to lack of interest.

We apologise to members of the local ballroom dancing society who turned up last Sunday at St Cliff's for any inconvenience caused.

The notice at the front of the church should have read 'Giving Sunday' and not 'Jiving Sunday'.

REQUESTS

Bird cage wanted for pensioner.

light s off when leaving the buildi the Property Committee's final warni members.

Police were called to St Cliff's on Monday morning to investigate a report of vandalism in the church's youth room. The local constabulary were summoned by Mrs Willock who had just begun her first day serving on the church's cleaning rota.

The shocked lady was given the rest of the day off after telling WPC Biggs (no relation) of the terrible scene that met her eyes when she entered the room to clean it. Tables and chairs were upturned, graffiti was scrawled across the walls and the contents of the litter bin were strewn over the floor. Having been informed by Mrs Johnson (a more seasoned member of the cleaning team) that this was quite normal for the youth room WPC Biggs promptly closed the case and left the premises.

we will ensure that bouyancy e at all future baptismal

It is with great pleasure that we can announce he birth of quadruplets to Mr and Mrs Jones

At our AGM last Wednesday it was noted that St Cliff's can presently lay claim to at least twenty seven committees of one kind or other. In a bid to streamline our efforts it has been proposed that a Committees Committee be set up immediately to deal with this situation.

BOOK REVIEW

The Shack purports to be a Christian novel and to John Bunyan's

St. Cliff's
— Parish Church —

23 May 2010

Dear Mrs Cliffington

Thank you for your kind offer to lead St. Cliff's Day of Prayer this coming Saturday (2–4pm).

After much consideration, I feel that intercession is perhaps not your primary calling. I say this based upon the evidence of your contribution to last Sunday evening's 'Share-a-Prayer' service (a snappy title that I am rather proud of).

Being blessed with a rather fine cassette tape recorder at St. Cliff's (to retain my weekly sermons for posterity), we were also fortuitously able to magnetically capture your 'sample' prayer, which has aided my decision regarding your offer, and a transcript of which now follows:

'Dear Lord, I bring before You, metaphorically speaking that is, my husband's varicose veins which have been playing him up something rotten lately. As You know, he's been off work three times already this year from his part-time job at Iceland and he's at his wits' end. We've tried everything including a Softgrip Compression Stocking (RRP £19.75) as recommended by our local chemist. A waste of money if you ask me. It's done little to alleviate his considerable discomfort. Our next door neighbour, Mr Dobson (I think You know him, Lord), has offered to drive my afflicted husband to work, but if anyone at the church is free next Tuesday to give him a lift to the hospital for his regular check-up, it would be much appreciated as I am obliged to visit my elderly mother on that particular day. Her name is Mrs Potts for those of you who don't know her. Although she has settled into Twilight Villas (which is a twenty-four-hour, warden-controlled facility), her rheumatoid arthritis is playing her up terribly and I am a little surprised that nobody from the church has yet been round to see her. Between You and me, it would be really nice if the minister could pay her a visit, even though she's not C of E. Amen.'

May I humbly suggest a little tip that I have found most helpful when engaging in the activity of prayer:

Pray for something!

Onward and upward

Derek

What's missing ...?

28 May, 2010

Dear Friends

I readily raise my hand and confess that within the body of this apparently respectable clergyman lurks an inner child just itching to get out.

This latent youthfulness recently sprang to life when, on passing the nearby United Reformed Church and noticing that the last vestiges of this once august building had been finally razed to the ground (with the aid of a very sizeable demolition ball) in readiness for their new building, I simply could not resist scribbling a minor amendment to the dog-eared and faded poster that adorned the lonely wayside pulpit, the last witness to its existence.

Seemingly ignorant of the fact that there was now no church to be publicised, it resolutely proclaimed to one and all that time-honoured (and corny) message favoured of many a church, namely, **'CH_ _ CH. WHAT'S MISSING? UR'**.

Utilising the convenient indelible marker pen that lay resident within my jacket pocket (having been confiscated from young Wayne Peacock whom I had caught in the process of similarly appending a mugshot of myself that graces St. Cliff's 'Welcome Desk', with a Groucho Marx-esque moustache – which, I should add, did not suit me in the least), I cheekily crossed out the second letter 'C' (so that it read CH_ _ _H), then added the letter 'C' to the end of 'UR' to reflect the present state of this church.

I trust that those passing by this temporarily defunct ecclesiastical establishment will appreciate the cleverness of my witty word play.

I also trust that St. Cliff's Property Committee will take a leaf out of the book of our URC brethren, and consider likewise bringing our ancient meeting place into the twenty-first century.

Onward and upward

Derek

Must have a word with Mr Bargepole our churchwarden and remind him that we are not in South London (from whence he hails) and thus to refrain from referring to me as Del Boy!

The spectre of yesteryear!

31 May, 2010

Dear Friends

Once again summer is upon us and, unlike December, this is most definitely not the season to be jolly – that is if you happen to be of school age and are presently bracing yourself for the fearful onslaught of examinations.

For myself, this month stirs up the ghosts of some rather uncomfortable memories of my not-so-halcyon college days.

The manse Slumberwell Deluxe Orthopaedic Divan (which is normally the nocturnal residence of not only yours truly but also my nearest and dearest) abruptly becomes an empty wasteland of quilted polyester, with but one incumbent to suffer the ravages of this super-sprung monster. My good lady wife, in the pursuit of an undisturbed night's sleep, decamps for this unfortunate month to the box room from whence she will only return once my tortuous and, I have to agree, sweaty tossings and turnings have been exorcised for yet another year.

These spectres of yesteryear are no doubt only guaranteed their annual reawakening courtesy of an abnormally heavy burden of guilt which would make even John Bunyan's pilgrim feel positively light across his shoulders.

I have to confess that, when entering the examination room way back when to complete the final essay of what had turned out to be a remarkably unremarkable second year at St Winifred's Theological Institute, I was blissfully unaware that 'Blood Sacrifices in a Vegetarian Society' was not the only essay topic being tackled that day. Not only did my mind go completely blank when presented with the examination paper, but so also did my conscience. Unable to recall even a single punctuation mark pertaining to my last twelve months of studies, I resorted to that final bastion of the desperate – I cheated!

The unfamiliar scholar to my left seemed completely unconcerned that his workmanship was visible to all-comers (namely my good self) and, not wishing to look the proverbial gift horse in the mouth, I bestowed upon him the highest honour to hand at that particular moment by confirming that imitation is indeed the sincerest form of flattery.

The whole experience turned out to be far more stimulating than I could ever have imagined. This young man was expounding ideas so new to me that I could only conclude they had been presented at St Winifred's when I was absent during one of my recurrent heavy earwax production episodes, and thus unable to hear a dickie bird.

If only time machines were not some fanciful, fictional concoction then the ensuing embarrassment could all too readily have been erased from the annals of history. This not being the case, I will have to live with the knowledge that the examination room, that fateful day, was also playing host to the local school of butchery. As a result, I catastrophically cribbed not a theological treatise but rather an essay disseminating (as terrible coincidence would have it) the congealed delights of the black pudding.

My penance of nocturnal torment is a price that I must pay.

Roll on July!

Onward and upward
Derek

Let the bidding war commence!
4 June, 2010

Dear Friends

It is all but three months since I embarked upon my journey into the, as then unfamiliar, 'blogosphere'.

Little did I imagine when I excitedly launched my first 'post' onto the airwaves of the World Wide Web that I would receive such a positive and encouraging response from my 'online' congregants. I have mused on perhaps more than one occasion that it is a pity that my sermons at St. Cliff's are not met so gladly and, for that matter, that the size of my flock does not nearly match that of my ever-increasing 'online' congregation.

Anyway, that is by the by for I am presently preoccupied with something that pushes such unhelpful thoughts far into the background.

The 'something' in question was inspired (in a roundabout sort of way) by a pastoral visit that I paid this morning to the home of old Mr McMurtry.

I had readily accepted his invitation to pop round for a cup of tea and a natter as we shook hands after last Sunday's service, mistakenly thinking that he wanted to give me a pat on the back for my detailed exposition on the baptism in the Holy Spirit.

What I hadn't realised was that he was in the process of wearing in a new set of false teeth and was thus not actually *commending* me (as it had seemed to my eager ears as I strained to catch what he was saying between the irritating clicking of his dentures), but rather he was roundly *condemning* me for my particular theological stance.

The fellow was in fact of the dispensationalist persuasion and was therefore keen to have the matter out with me (over the aforementioned cuppa).

That his dentures had been returned to the dentist for some

emergency fine tuning was a relief indeed, and saved us both the dribbly embarrassment of his attempting to converse with a pair of loose and limp lips. I seized my chance and quickly scoured the room for some inspiration for casual (and most definitely non dispensationalist) conversation, and my eyes immediately set upon a copy of *The Diary of Samuel Pepys*, which lay gathering dust at one end of Mr McMurtry's piano (the castor having apparently gone A.W.O.L.).

Whilst I will admit that not all of the book's content is perhaps suitable discourse for a clergyman, I succeeded in waffling on about the Great Fire of London (a subject touched upon by the diarist) long enough to finish my scalding cup of tea (and its accompanying soggy biscuit) and hastily bid my temporarily muted antagonist a hearty farewell.

It was as I journeyed back to the manse that thoughts of Mr Pepys' esteemed journal began to race enticingly around my head.

If the regular ramblings of this familiar gentleman were deemed of interest to the good people of the literary establishment, then perhaps it would not be such an incredulous notion for the missives of yours truly to likewise appear between the covers of a book.

Stilling all thoughts, as best I can, of one day being as well known as Ms J.K. Rowling (but without resorting to the darker realms for my subject matter), I have decided to throw caution to the proverbial wind and to make my 'online' missives available to a wider readership, far beyond even that of St. Cliff's Weekly News Sheet, which I am informed by the editor is now well into 'double figures'.

I gather from the little that I know of matters literary that it is standard practice for publishers to compete for the opportunity to produce the work of a particular author (such as myself).

To that end, I have decided to invite the interest of publishers who would like to produce what I have presently entitled, 'A Year at St. Cliff's'.

Let the bidding war commence!

Onward and upward
Derek

Post Scriptum. I see from a cursory glance at one or two of the books presently littering my study that books frequently bear testimonials from 'supporters' of the author's work. To that end, and as an added incentive to any potential publisher considering my literary wares, I may ask Mrs Smith, who reviews selected tomes for St. Cliff's Weekly News Sheet, if she would kindly add her valuable endorsement to my work. It should be known that a favourable report of Messrs Butterworth and Inkpen's latest biblical compendium rendered St. Cliff's bookstall devoid of its two copies within a week.

A tad embarrassing!
12 June, 2010
Dear Friends

Having recently overhauled St. Cliff's somewhat lacklustre and faith-deficient prayer ministry team so thoroughly that even the Early Church would have taken note (and by that I am not alluding to St. Mary's up the road who have added an 8am service in an attempt to cream off the Sunday 'trade'), it is none other than my good self who has now gone and let the side down.

In fairness to me, the gentleman who came forward for prayer last Sunday was inclined to talk extremely quietly and, whilst it might have appeared that my attentive and forward-leaning posture was one of empathy and concern, it was in fact nothing of the sort. More an attempt (and an unsuccessful one at that) to discover what on earth the mumbling fellow was saying.

Rather than send him away 'empty-handed', I finally decided to plump for my best guess at what he was asking me to pray for. Laying my hand on his bald pate, I proceeded to command the renewal of the absent hair follicles – much to his surprise, I might add.

It was only after I had pronounced a hearty and faith-filled 'amen' that I discovered (to my utter embarrassment) that the gentleman had actually wanted me to pray for his family whose pet rabbit had recently passed away, and thus for '*their* loss' and not, as I had mistakenly imagined, his '*hair* loss'.

I think I will probably absent myself from the prayer ministry rota for the next week or two until its reputation is once more restored.

Onward and upward
Derek

Oh deary me!
15 June, 2010
Dear Friends

I fear that it will be some time before I recover from the embarrassment of my gargantuan gaffe on Sunday morning.

As the time came for me to close our morning service, my mind went completely blank and for the life of me I simply could not remember a single word of our traditional 'close of play' blessing.

Rather than wait a moment for my flustered brain to get itself together, my mouth decided to have a stab at it of its own volition.

That, 'Bless 'em all, bless 'em all, the long and the short and the tall', should be the best I could muster will haunt me for many a day.

Onward and upward
Derek

More haste!
21 June, 2010
Dear Friends

Though I do say so myself, our fish suppers at St. Cliff's take some beating (or should I say 'battering'?), and what a joy it was that all but twenty souls with a penchant for Britain's finest fare should grace us with their presence on the occasion of this week's ever-popular 'Food 'n' Fellowship' evening.

What I did not realise was that our regular purveyors of fish and chips were unable to fulfil their monthly order (an 'off' jumbo sausage having unfortunately contaminated their prized batter) and that St. Cliff's Catering Committee therefore had little choice but to make an executive decision and to give our considerable business to their only rivals in the town.

That until now we have boycotted the somewhat inappropriately named The Piece of Cod will not surprise you, but on this occasion it was a case of any port in a storm and expediency won the day.

The warmth of the evening necessitated the opening of windows, which made the surreptitious disposal of the less-than-satisfactory fish suppers all too easy for our guests.

It was not until the next day that I discovered that the grounds of St. Cliff's were not only littered with numerous half-eaten cod portions but also an equal quantity of salivating cats.

I now think that I was perhaps a little hasty in purchasing something which I thought would 'do the job' of ridding the church's hallowed precincts of this unexpected feline plague.

It would appear that I misunderstood the nature of the product to hand and, having sprinkled it liberally around the confines of St. Cliff's, I was rather troubled to discover that the invasion of cats had significantly increased in number and not diminished as I had hoped.

I now find that Go-Cat is in fact a food product and not something to send the pesky creatures packing.

Onward and upward
Derek

Annual Clergy Sports Day looms large!
I must remember to lay off the hay fever tablets in the preceding days.
That the bishop was tested for 'Lem Sip' after last year's Egg and Spoon Race is caution enough.

Derek had a quicker way to settle theological disputes!

Our cup runneth over!
1 July, 2010

Dear Friends

Our cup at St. Cliff's verily runneth over. What saintly task have we performed to have had bestowed upon us such an unwarranted blessing as this? It is not every day that a celebrity will venture off the beaten track to somewhere like St. Cliff's, and thus the imminent arrival of one Sir Cliff Richard, no less, to pair up with the bishop's wife in the Annual Roof Fund Tennis Tournament has, it must be said, caused quite a stir.

I confess to not being 'up' with popular music, preferring the resonant tones of Mr Roger Whittaker – as a bit of a whistler myself (much to the annoyance of my dear wife who, not being inclined to encourage my mastery of this most natural of musical instruments, has been known to rather unkindly compare my puckered offerings to the dying chorus of a marsh warbler) – and am unsure as to whether today's young folk are still tapping their toes to Mr Richard's inspiring melodies.

I will dust off the stylus of my gramophone player and pay an exploratory visit to the local record emporium at the earliest opportunity, lest I be accused of being out of touch with popular musical trends.

I must also make a mental note to inform Mr Meridew, the groundsman at the Charles Darwin Memorial Recreation Ground (whose name, it must be said, was only tenuously arrived at by its being sited adjacent to the now defunct World of Finches bird outlet), that we wish to pre-book two concurrent sessions of tennis on Court One for the affixed day. In doing so, I do recognise that sub-section two in the Borough Council's Rules and Regulations for the Booking of Municipal Sports Facilities expressly forbids this practice.

However, of all strange coincidences, Mr Meridew, in his youth, played the lead in the Piddlingdale District Council Operatic Society's rendition of *Summer Holiday*, so an amicable resolve has therefore been found to the offending piece of red tape, which we have now satisfactorily bypassed.

This is all thanks to the promise of a signed copy of Mr Richard's chart-topping 'Devil Woman', which the bishop's wife inadvertently purchased at a Women's Institute bazaar two years previously. Realising what she had bought, the flustered lady hastily locked it away in her spare room ready to be dealt with by the Diocesan Exorcism Committee the next time they met.

A rather unfortunate incident involving the Reverend Cribbins (the aforementioned Committee's chairman), the Parish Whist Society and a rogue pack of tarot cards (which were mistakenly dealt as playing cards) secured the Exorcism Committee's prompt demise, preserving the personalised recording from rigorous scrutiny for traces of devilish back-tracking, and thus releasing the piece of vinyl in question to be used as a gift to oil the wheels of bureaucracy.

Let us pray that the weather is kind to us when 'Cliff' descends upon us, and that we are spared from being overrun with screaming teeny boppers, which I gather are now the order of the day when it comes to popular music celebrities.

Onward and upward
Derek

71

Don't leave me this way!
2 July, 2010

Dear Friends

Being a relative novice with regard to all things technological, I was unaware of the painful reality of losing 'friends' on the Facebook World Wide Web social networking portal.

It has long been the lot of those entrusted with pastoring Jesus' Church to both enjoy the influx of new members to the congregation via the welcoming arms of a church's front entrance, whilst facing up to the inevitable loss of others through the oft equally accessible back door.

I will admit that I haven't been keeping a weather eye on my Facebook 'tally' of late, having been rightly cautioned that the practice of numbering landed King David in a spot of bother, but it is clear to me that, whilst continually receiving requests for my internet friendship, there are some who are quietly slinking out of the back door unnoticed.

Having toyed with the idea of seeking to 'drum up' a bit more trade to lift my spirits, I have resisted and instead opted to remind myself that all the affirmation I need comes from my relationship with my heavenly Father.

Onward and upward

Derek

Post Scriptum. That said, it would be churlish to deny that more companions are always most welcome!

The right hand of fellowship!

12 July, 2010

Dear Friends

We have much to be grateful for at St. Cliff's, not least that our much-publicised Summer Fete should have passed by with few of the traumas of last year's embarrassing debacle.

I sometimes feel that there are those among us who would readily replace the rainbow-coloured (though perhaps a tad dated), embroidered 'Welcome' banner which adorns St. Cliff's porch with the harsher tones of a 'Trespassers Will Be Prosecuted' sign. My suspicions were proven to be well-founded when a visitor to our traditional summer extravaganza made the mistake of finding themselves first in line at the legendary cake stall.

What the unfortunate lady was not privy to was that the matriarchs of St. Cliff's consider it a privilege of rank (assumed by their longevity within the church) to have 'first pickings' of the sumptuous display of calorie-laden pastries and cakes.

That the visitor in question had a sweet tooth (at least that is what I concluded from a brief glimpse of her filling-encrusted choppers) did nothing to help matters. In fact, when presented with the opportunity to remove herself from the vicinity until the aforementioned matriarchs had secured the 'cream of the crop', she simply crossed her arms, cocked her head and dared her adversaries to 'try and make me'.

It is thanks to the foresight of our somewhat overly safety-conscious administrator, Mr Merryview, that each year we are blessed by the attendance of the good folk of St. John's Ambulance, who are on hand to offer succour and balm to the afflicted. On this particular occasion, their life-giving ministrations were required to attend to the blackened eye of this 'cake stall interloper' (as some would have it), who had subsequently been offered the right hand of fellowship (albeit in a clenched form) by the ring leader of the offended matriarchal mob.

What a blessing indeed that the photographer from our local paper was at that moment preoccupied with snapping the bishop, as he bungee-jumped from the bell tower.

Onward and upward
Derek

Derek endeavoured to make door-to-door evangelism self-funding!

St. Cliff's
— Parish Church —

19 July 2010

Dear Mr Griffiths

Thank you for your kind letter expressing appreciation for my recent talk to the **Senior Citizens Lunch Club**.

I have to say that I felt very much inspired to preach on Abraham's faith to have a son in old age and I hoped that it would encourage a renewed trust in God for my audience.

It was, therefore, a bit of a surprise to me when your letter arrived on the doormat of the manse, informing me that you and Mrs Griffiths (who I believe are both seasoned octogenarians) are planning to add to your already sizeable family. I would like to add a note of caution to your startling suggestion and also to retract my throw-away line that there's 'life in the old dog yet'. That this is not scriptural, but rather an idiomatic adage, should suffice to nip your extremely concerning plans to procreate in the bud.

I fear that the residents of Twilight Villas, where you both reside, will also be less than sympathetic to infant cries through the watches of the night.

Can I suggest that you reconsider your 'expansion' plans post-haste and perhaps channel your faith-inspired energies into St. Cliff's Roof Fund instead? Like Abraham, it has been awaiting its hoped for fulfilment for many a year but, unlike that father of the faith, we have seen quite enough of the starry host through its gaping holes.

Onward and upward

Derek

A bit of a blow!
19 July, 2010
Dear Friends

With such a favourable run of weather of late, I considered it an ideal opportunity to lay on a barbecue for the good folk of the community.

Since the local craft fair had been rained off a few weeks earlier, I further indulged this uncommon bout of impulsive spontaneity on my part by also inviting the rained-off artisans to join us at our al fresco outreach event in the hope that they would provide some added colour to the occasion.

It was unfortunate indeed that Mr Harris, a rather difficult fellow who has had a thing or two against St. Cliff's since goodness knows when (particularly with regard to our habit of accompanying the dawn chorus with a peal of bells), should choose this particular day to bury the hatchet and offer to lend a hand with the cooking.

Had I but known that he sported a glass eye and that it had a ghastly habit of regularly falling out, I would have immediately redeployed him to the 'relishes and ketchup' table and thus avoided the ensuing calamity.

Who could have foreseen that at the very moment his ill-fitting orb should choose to wriggle loose from its socket and plummet into the waiting fiery embers, a gentleman from the glass-blowing demonstration should choose to take a break and partake of a burger?

Not wishing to pass up this impromptu opportunity to demonstrate his craft, he swiftly extricated Mr Harris's molten eye from its meaty companions and proceeded to 'do his stuff', as he put it. That this 'stuff' should take the form of re-shaping the glass eye into a small (though, I have to say, rather attractive) vase did nothing to appease the ire of its owner. Nor did my offer of a free hot dog with two servings of fried onions (one serving being the advertised quantity).

I expect that it is only a matter of time before our bell ringers get a visit from the folk at Environmental Health and with it, no doubt, an invitation to have an enforced morning lie-in henceforth.

Onward and upward
Derek

In response to my feature, 'Ask Derek', in which I offer to employ my experience and wisdom (such as it is) to answer church-related or theological conundrums, Darryn Lloyd from Australia asks ...

Dear Derek
How is it best to avoid the ever-present 'huggers'?

Dear Mr Lloyd
'Huggers' (Christians who have a proclivity to seek every opportunity to embrace anything that moves) are to be found in just about every church, so moving to another place of worship will almost certainly not solve the problem.

Be warned! These affable engulfers of the human form have a particular penchant for homing in on those of a less tactile disposition. The slightest hint of unease or twitchiness on your part will immediately alert them to your proximity and thus your claustrophobic fate is inevitable. You may think that you can avoid their innocent clutches but you are very much mistaken. Soon enough all will fall victim to their emboldened bodily bonhomie.

But, fear not, my antipodean congregant, all is not completely lost.

A firm handshake being the top end of my scale of preference for social contact, I have developed what I consider to be a foolproof means by which to stave off the threat of a 'hugger's' bearlike grip.

Having had the good fortune to purchase a second-hand badge-making kit at St. Cliff's recent 'Bring and Buy' sale (you will no doubt have guessed already that our ever-present Roof Fund was the grateful beneficiary), I hit upon producing a badge bearing the familiar (yet slightly foreboding) 'radiation' symbol, beneath which I placed the words (in the rather authoritative Helvetica Bold typeface), 'I love (but utilising the ubiquitous 'heart' symbol) Nuclear Power Stations'.

I have found that even the most ardent of huggers will show undue restraint when faced with the possibility of imminent irradiation.

I trust that this has been of some help but failing that, may I proffer a spot of time-honoured wisdom:

'If you can't beat them, join them.'

Onward and upward
Derek

The clouds are gathering!
29 July, 2010

Dear Friends

With less than forty-eight hours to go before we depart for Estuary View Holiday Village, I have been much concerned that our week-long sojourn could well be destined for that unwelcome fixture of the British summer season, namely, 'mixed weather'.

In a last minute bid to stay the forces of darkness, so to speak, I decided upon prayer walking around the brochure which features the above-mentioned holiday utopia (or so it is portrayed).

Whilst I paced the floor in heated (and heartfelt) intercession, my wife slipped into the room, unbeknownst to me, and placed my cup of elevenses at my pounding feet.

You will not need to be a student of the comedic arts to imagine what ensued, save to say that Estuary View Holiday Village is no longer the 'sun-soaked' location that the artisans of the airbrush would have us believe, but rather a murky and damp row of drab chalets (thanks to my spilled cup of coffee) which nobody in their right mind would part with good money to stay the night in, let alone for a week.

My attempts to dispel the foreboding and fatalistic barrage of thoughts that are now assaulting my mind as a consequence of this coffee-fuelled deluge are certainly not helped by the words of Graham Kendrick's popular ditty, 'O Lord, the clouds are gathering', which has chosen this particular moment to take up residence in my head.

I will proceed to my gramophone collection forthwith and see if I can find my copy of another of Mr Kendrick's popular works, 'Shine, Jesus, Shine', in the hope that perhaps the situation might be turned around even at this late stage.

Onward and upward

Derek

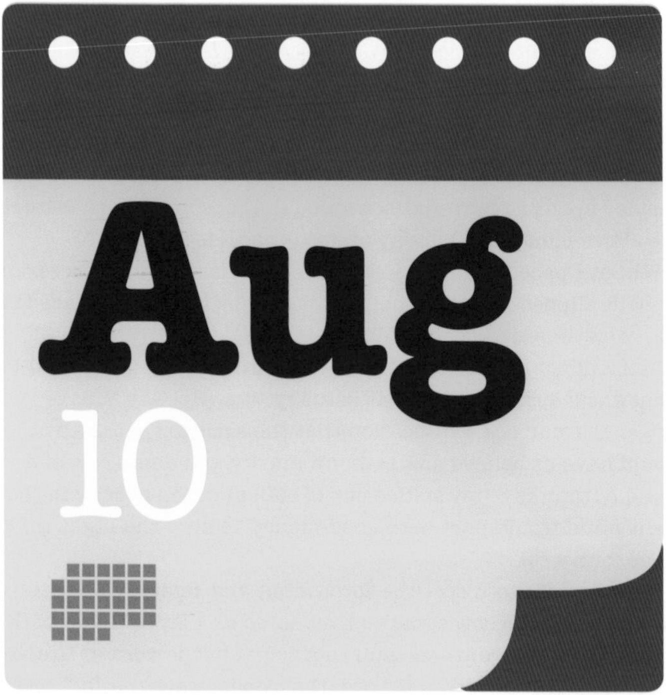
Aug
10

A change is as good as a rest!
2 August, 2010
Dear Friends

'A change', so the old adage goes, 'is as good as a rest.'

Unfortunately, I cannot vouch for the validity of this sweeping generality as I am, what the other old adage identifies as, 'the exception that proves the rule'.

I write to you from the cramped and rather damp confines of our 'luxury' caravan at the Estuary View Holiday Village, where my good lady wife and I have come to recharge our ecclesiastical batteries.

I confess to having yet to enjoy what the brochure somewhat elastically refers to as the 'sun-kissed golden sands', and instead have only managed to delight in the rain-soaked utility block which is positioned but four feet from our window.

Our plans to visit a local church were scuppered when Mr Bradshaw, the proprietor of this latter day Colditz, discovered that a man of the cloth was in residence and promptly volunteered my services to lead the Hallelujah Hour. This is his desperate attempt to keep any of the faithful amongst the inmates from escaping to the village church and thereby chancing on the myriad B&Bs that line the village street, whereupon they might succumb to the lure of their warm and homely charm.

I can only but think that the Hallelujah Hour derives its name from the cry of relief that goes forth once these sixty painful minutes are up. It is a preacher's worst nightmare to be faced with a congregation whose constituents are but one man and his dog. It must be presumed that on this particular day, one half of this infamous duo was off chasing rabbits or some such canine pursuit. This left just me and Mr Jolly, the resident white coat (a bleaching accident having drained away every last colourful memory of his days at Butlins), to go through the motions.

I was beginning to wonder how two unaccompanied voices might survive the rigours of Mr Bradshaw's extensive list of suggested hymns (my wife and able pianist being bedridden with a suspiciously sudden outbreak of something vague), when Mr Jolly whipped out from his top pocket two teaspoons which he proceeded to play, without respite, for the duration.

The trauma of his interminable clattering was such that I fear there are some hymns I may never be able to enjoy again.

The upside of this was that, unbeknownst to me, Mr Bradshaw had taken it upon himself to pipe this calamitous hour to the furthest corners of the site, and not only was Mr Jolly's dubious talent heard by a holidaying minion of the *Songs of Praise* television programme's production team, but Mr Jolly has also now secured himself a slot when the show comes to the area next spring.

The fact that *Songs of Praise* is broadcast at precisely the same time as St. Cliff's evening service is something for which I will be ever grateful.

Onward and upward
Derek

Humble pie!
8 August, 2010
Dear Friends

How unfortunate that so soon after returning from our holiday (albeit a blighted one) I should slip back so readily into my unfortunate habit of 'putting my foot in it'.

The aged stalwart of a church cooker at St. Cliff's choosing the week of our absence to finally give up the ghost was quite unhelpful, not least in that tomorrow sees the commencement of our annual holiday club.

This week-long invasion of overly exuberant children has its chief selling point in the daily provision of a hot lunch, which we generously serve free of charge (a hard-fought battle in this respect having been won along the way with our less-than-faith-filled treasurer). Whilst some have accused us of flagrantly enticing 'clientele' away from the holiday clubs that other churches have laid on within the town, I would humbly refute the charge. I rest easy in the knowledge that sheep will always graze on the pasture that is greenest.

With the urgency of a resolve in respect of the sadly defunct cooker utmost in my mind, it seemed almost too good to be true that, as this morning's congregation eased their way through the cramped confines of St. Cliff's entrance, I should overhear a visitor to our fair parish identify himself as a gas fitter. In that time was of the essence, I felt it acceptable to interrupt the flow of conversation and commandeer the gentleman's services immediately.

Ignoring his protests that I had got the wrong man (believing it to be just a spot of self-deprecation on his part), I whisked him off to the kitchen. There I left him to make an initial assessment of whether, like Lazarus, the failed apparatus could be brought back from the dead, while I headed off to the church office to hunt down a requisition order in the hope of getting the job done before he left the premises.

On my return I was somewhat surprised to find that the said tradesman had not lifted so much as a finger. I can only consider it a blessing indeed that I did not launch forth into a diatribe about what I considered the oft *laissez faire* attitude of many such fellows nowadays.

As I drew breath to vent my spleen, the gracious gentleman seized the moment and said that he thought there had been a bit of a misunderstanding. He explained that he was in fact not a gas fitter by profession, but rather a gastroenterologist at the local hospital.

This embarrassing saga was only made worse by the uneasy feeling I have that he was in the final stages of accepting an invitation to our autumn Alpha course when I apprehended him.

To my chagrin I will now need to break to our Alpha representative the *faux pas* I have committed, which has probably deprived them of another 'taker' for the course. Not only is there every likelihood that will I be eating humble pie for some considerable time, but the way things presently stand with the cooker, there is every chance that it will be cold.

Onward and upward

Derek

Derek's early morning quiet time was going great guns!

St. Cliff's
— Parish Church —

12th August 2010

Dear Mr Lee

Further to your enquiry as to the possibility of the weekly hire of St. Cliff's church hall, I am afraid that, after consideration, we are unable to offer you the use of this facility.

On the basis of your original correspondence, we did feel that the opportunity for husbands and wives to take part in a range of creative activities fitted well within our aims to support the institution of marriage.

Your subsequent letter correcting your typing error has somewhat changed our thinking on this matter and thus, unfortunately, our response.

Can I suggest that, before you entrust any future correspondence to the Royal Mail, you perhaps take the time to proof read the intended content.

Whilst we are more than happy to allow our venue to be hired for the purposes of marital arts, we are not able to do so for the propagation of martial arts.

Onward and upward

Derek

Derek

A fishy business!
16 August, 2010
Dear Friends

Having been challenged of late by my good lady wife with respect to what she claims are my lacklustre attempts to foster the spirit of ecumenism within our fair parish, I resolved (perhaps a tad reluctantly, I will confess) to make a little more effort in this respect.

A brief foray to the local shops to replace my emergency supply of Trebor Mints presented me with an opportunity for the rubber to hit the proverbial road. I should add in passing that fresh breath (of the minty variety) is now a top priority within St. Cliff's prayer ministry team since an unfortunate 'punter' was laid low, not by the power of God, but rather by the less-than-savoury, and most certainly all-consuming, breath of one of our number.

On entering Fags and Mags, the nearest purveyors of the aforementioned minty morsels, I could not believe my good fortune in being presented with such a ready opportunity to engage with a fellow believer. Whilst I did think it a little odd that the man in question was buying up lottery tickets as if there was no tomorrow, I shelved any unhelpful inclination I might have had to judge a Christian brother and, as he turned to make his exit, I flung my open arms around him in the manner of the father in the parable of the prodigal son, clasping the gentleman to my chest in a vice-like embrace.

Things did not turn out quite as I would have hoped, and his immediate suspicion was that he was in the process of being mugged rather than entering into an act of ecumenical harmony. This impression was only abated by his catching sight of my protruding dog collar. I shudder to think what he would have done with his hastily clenched fist otherwise.

In a bid to shed light on this temporary misunderstanding, I quickly pointed to my icthus 'fish' badge that matched his similar shaped silver lapel badge (this being my rationale for identifying the chap as a fellow believer in the first place).

Sadly I was mistaken.

It turns out that my ecumenical advances were in vain and what he was in fact sporting was the mark of a garden shears salesman and not a brother in Christ.

To add to my shame, the unconvinced proprietor of Fags and Mags has slapped his own version of an ASBO on my good self for the duration of one month (subject to good behaviour), after which I will be allowed back into his shop.

Let us hope that the prayer line at St. Cliff's is a little lighter this summer season while the opportunity to replenish my mint supply is temporarily put on hold.

Onward and upward

Derek

Inter-Church Spelling Contest tomorrow night. Must teach St. Cliff's team to spell that tricky word **Ecumenism** if we're going to be in with half a chance of wiping the floor with the lot of 'em!

24 August, 2010

Worla of Anglicanism

⊕ SITUATIONS VACANT

Full Time Youth Worker

Traditional but forward-thinking Anglican church (a veritable faith statement
on my part) desperately seeks youth worker to replace our retiring youth
deacon whose recently imposed nine o'clock nursing home curfew now
makes continuing in this role untenuous.

This is most assuredly a post for someone who has the vision for expansion,
our youth group being somewhat thin on the ground at present (six at the
last tally I will admit if you count Jason Watkins who will be joining us in
September from the primary department).

In that two thirds of our young people are not from these shores a second
language (preferably Polish) would also be an asset.
Sadly 'tongues' does not count in this instance although its usage at St Cliff's
will be encouraged by myself although not by our small but hardened band
of entrenched dispensationalists who are wont to employ every frowning
facial muscle at their disposal to display their intense disapproval of 'them
there heretics' as they deem those of us of the 'Spirit-filled' variety.

We would prefer you to have no body piercings (these have a tendency to
make me feel a little queasy) but a baseball hat in reverse position (which I
am informed denotes complicity with the younger generation) would be a
distinct advantage.

Additionally the ability to play a 'modern' instrument such as the guitar
(electric even better to drown out Mrs Higginbottom on the organ) would
be invaluable.

Salary to be confirmed (which is another way of saying that I have yet to
pluck up courage to broach the funding of this new position with our
treasurer).

Applications to:
Derek the Cleric
St Cliff's
PO Box 666
(Please read nothing into this unfortunate number configuration)

28 August, 2010

From	d_asbo_king@yahoo.co.uk
Cc	
BCC	
To	derekthecleric@hotmail.co.uk
Subject	yoof wrkR job

I iz replying 2 ur advert 4 a yoof wrkR.
I av bn outa wrk sinC i lft skool lst yr so i reckon dat dis wld B a gd mve
2 gt d job centA off my bac coz dey kip hassling me bout stuf lk hngn ot
on d streets wiv my m8s n doiN graffiti n stuf.
It l%ks 2 me lk ur yoof posse nEdz a gd leader lk w@ i iz n f u wn2 giv
me d job thN i wld brng wiv me my own posse 2 Nsure nun of d oder
yoof groups frm d oder churches giv em ne grief f u knw w@ i mean.
i dnt do no oder langwiges lk u askD 4 bt i iz real gd @ inglish.
I also iz no gd @ muzc bt f u wn2 av somit 2 blast ur organist outa
d plce big tym thN i iz a rt QL dj.

O yea + i iz also hpE 2 Bcum a xtian f dis hlps me gt d job.

D Asbo King

To	d_asbo_king@yahoo.co.uk
Cc	
BCC	
From	derekthecleric@hotmail.co.uk
Subject	re:yoof wrkR job

Dear Mr King

Thank you for your recent application for the post of 'yoof wrkR' (as you put it) at St Cliff's church.

Whilst you have admitted that you do not operate in the gift of tongues I have to confess that on this occasion its companion gift of interpretation appears to have gone A.W.O.L also and for the life of me I could not make head nor tail of the majority of your mysterious communication.

I am not sure that St Cliff's is quite ready for your 'posse' nor indeed your apparent offer of the ministry of threats and menaces against the other youth groups that serve this fair parish.

In that you are also clearly not yet 'one of us' perhaps I can be so bold as to mention that 'Alpha at St Cliff's' begins afresh this autumn. If you do wish to attend can I ask that you fill in the application form using a rendering of the English language that all of us can understand. A few more vowels per word would be an asset.

I wish you well in your search for gainful employment and in closing can I ask that if you are indeed the person who has been appending our church notice board with the contents of a spray can (you expressed a penchant for the art of graffiti) will you cease that practice immediately. Your editing of 'Sunday Services' to render it 'Sinday Services was really most unhelpful.

Onward and upward

Derek

Carruther's Cakes

— CONFECTION PERFECTION —

1/9/10

Dear Reverend

I am writing in response to your quarter page advertisement for a youth worker in *World of Anglicanism* to which I have just renewed my annual subscription in the hope that this will swing it for me.

Having recently been signed off with stress by the doctor from my work at Carruther's Confectionery, where I was a Glazed Cherry Positioning Operative in the Bakewell Tart Department, I find that I now have more time on my hands than I know what to do with. Thus something to fill my days would come in really handy.

I have asked my wife her thoughts on this matter and she thinks that I would be more than suitable for the job, although I am not sure whether this is just a ploy on her part to get me out of the house when she holds her regular seances. I have put my foot down on this matter and have told her that, should I get the job, it might well require our home being opened to the young people of your church, and that she should consider inviting them along to one or two of her sessions.

My experience with children and young people is a little limited and we have not had any of our own to practise on. That said, I am sure that the ample experience I have with our preferred two dogs, two cats, two goldfish, two parrots and two guinea pigs is a transferable skill.

You made mention of the fact that this was a full-time position but you did not specify which days were to be worked. As I presently run the local crown green bowls club youth team (under 55s) which meets on a Sunday morning, I would need to stipulate in my conditions of work that I couldn't make it for your church services.

I trust this would not be a problem.

In anticipation of an interview for the post I have been to the library to read up on youngsters. I am just hoping that not too much has changed on the youth culture landscape since *Getting On Down With The Kids* was written in 1979.

I look forward to your reply.

Sincerely

Mr Charles Morris CoGCO (Confederation of Glazed Cherry Operatives)
P.s. I am 53.
P.p.s. I am more than happy to sport a reverse-facing baseball hat as requested in your advertisement. It will provide me with a bit of variety from my usual toupé.

Six months!

5 September, 2010

Dear Friends

Just a short missive to mark this momentous day, it being a veritable six months to the day since I first bravely launched myself on to the 'blogosphere'.

Since that wondrous moment, my congregation of the airwaves has outstripped that of my charge, St. Cliff's.

Let us hope that the bishop has noted this increase in my fruitfulness and that he sees fit to up my annual Christmas bonus (preferably in pounds sterling and not the usual ten pound Superdrug gift voucher).

There really is only so much verruca ointment a clergyman can buy!

Onward and upward

Derek

concerned that once again foreign currency and buttons have been found in the offering plate.

A reminder to one and all that our next prayer walk around the town will be this Saturday morning convening at 9am in the church car park.

Following a number of injuries last month which included an ankle sprain caused by stepping off a pavement awkwardly and a black eye and bloodied nose as a result of colliding with a lamp post can I remind all those taking part that in the interests of safety they will need to ensure that when praying it is not necessary to adhere to the tradition of closing one's eyes.

The Senior Citizens Bible study group will begin a series looking at the life of Methuselah and if anyone knows the whereabouts of the lost property box please could they inform the church office.

Regulars at St Cliff's will be heartened to hear that our treasurer has agreed to fund the purchase of Trebor Extra Strong Mints for use by the prayer ministry team.

It would appear that the recent increase of those 'going down' whilst being prayed for at the end of our Sunday morning services can now be wholly attributed to an unfortunate case of halitosis from which one of their number had been suffering and not the move of God that we optimistically supposed.

and everyone is welcome to our St George's Day curry night where we will be celebratin all things English.

Following pressure from the local Metho church the town wide monthly ecumenical and worship service will no longer be c 'The Happy Hour'.

On Wednesday at 8pm we will be meeting at the manse to continue our ever popular series on predestination. This week we will be looking at Calvanism and its belief in God's unconditional election.

Unfortunately this meeting will be by invitation only.

pleased to hear that Mr Johnson's black eye is recovering after unfortunately suffering a black eye during the singing of 'Wide, wide as the ocean'.

A hearty thank you to all who helped at St Cliff's Annual Summer Fete.

s Sunday the practice of leaving belongings on pews to reserve t

A respectable £423.16p was raised for the Roof Fund. (Whilst the progress towards our ambitious target is somewhat sluggish let us hope that it can be achieved before the Second Coming).

The winner of the 'Best Sandwich Sponge' competition was Mrs Pickles from the Baptist church thus scuppering our own Mrs Parsley-Smythe's hopes of winning it three times in a row. We were a tad disappointed that Mrs Parsley-Smythe did not accept defeat as gracefully as we might have hoped and her unexpected lunge at the new champion was not the right hand of fellowship that we might have hoped for.

The winner of the 35cl of malt whisky raffle prize, a gentleman from the local Methodist church, wishes to remain anonymous for two rather obvious reasons.

Without a shadow of a doubt the biggest crowd-puller of the day was our 'Soak the Bishop' sideshow. It did not escape the attention of many that our vicar appeared to spend rather a lot of his stipend on throwing water-soaked sponges at his superior.

Cliff's
BOARD

St Cliff's worship band wasn't what you'd call conventional!

and Christian Unity Week meetings are being held this Thurday at 8pm here or at the Methodist church.

With effect from next Sunday the prayer ministry team will be relocated to operate away from the vicinity of the worship band.

This is as a result of a misunderstanding last Sunday which occurred when, due to the overly loud volume emanating from the band, a visitor to the church was unfortunately 'misdiagnosed' as requesting prayer for a hernia.

It was only after ten minutes of fevered ministry that he was able to explain that he had recently been made redundant and was in fact seeking prayer for well paid work to keep up his mortgage payments, as he had been a 'high earner'.

FOR SALE

Pair of siamese cats. Offers. Cannot separate.
Tel 01

St. Cliff's
— Parish Church —

8th September 2010

Dear Mr Morris

Thank you for your recent application for the position of Full Time Youth Worker at St. Cliff's.

After much consideration, I have to inform you that I will not be inviting you for an interview.

A few things militate against your application and perhaps these are worth bearing in mind should you feel inclined to look for a youth-orientated post elsewhere in the parish.

First, some experience of working with young people (or even having some children of your own on which to practise, as you put it) would be a distinct advantage. Your knowledge of all things animal would on this occasion be of little practical use for the job, with the exception of your ability to have some empathy with Noah (in the unlikely event of your ever being called upon to teach from this particular passage in Genesis).

Secondly, I must tell you that your misplaced offer of an entrée for the young folk into the dubious world of necromancy has not helped your cause, nor has your inability to attend Sunday morning services at St. Cliff's. I presently have a situation where many of my flock are all too quick to exempt themselves from my sermons, and I would trust that any under my employ would be the first to take the lead in stemming this worrying tide of Sunday morning absenteeism.

Finally, without sounding rude, I was rather hoping for a candidate for the post who was at least half your age, and thus the offer to sport a reverse-facing baseball hat as a sign of complicity with the younger generation (in your case to cover an obvious bald patch) is not relevant.

Yours sincerely

Derek

Post Scriptum. Not only will your renewed annual subscription to *World of Anglicanism* not 'swing it' (I am not to be bought I will have you know), but your ill-judged gift of 'six individually wrapped Bakewell tarts' delivered this morning by a gentleman from DHL is already wending its way to St. Cliff's for summary disposal at our popular 'Cuppa and a Cake' morning tomorrow.

Post Post Scriptum. In that you are no longer in their employ, I suggest your use of Carruther's Confectionery stationery to be highly inappropriate.

I live in hope!
10 September, 2010
Dear Friends,

After embarking on a search for a permanent youth worker for St. Cliff's needy young folk, I feel that I have hit somewhat of an impasse. I daily wait with eager anticipation, perchance that the good folk of the Royal Mail will pop a favourable application through the manse letter box but, as yet, there has been nothing excepting that which I have shared with you previously.

Until that day when a worthy candidate should appear, I must be single-minded and focus on the task at hand, namely preparation for this Sunday's sermon in which I bring to a close my enlightening series on 'Leviticus Highlights'.

I have saved 'dreaded skin diseases' until the very end in a bid to hold the attention of our oft-bored youngsters. The last thing I need now is for them to take flight before a successful applicant comes to my aid.

I will keep you abreast of any progress.

Onward and upward

Derek

Post Scriptum. Then again, perhaps I will not put paid to 'Leviticus Highlights' quite yet. One can never have too much of 'infectious diseases' when it comes to keeping my flock on the straight and narrow.

Hey, I'd really love that job you're advertising!

You've probably had loads of better qualified applicants but in case you're interested, I've got a 1st in Applied Theology, a Diploma in Christian youth work and spent the last year on a youth evangelism team in Albania. x Millie x

P.S. Sorry about my application being on a napkin. I'm witnessing to a bunch of kids in MacDonald's right now. :)

Mob: 0170

18 Sep 2010 09:05:52

Dear Millie.
When can you start?
Derek

Coming a crop-per!
22 September, 2010
Dear Friends

It has been said by some person or other that all roads lead to Rome. It must also be said that, as far as St. Cliff's is concerned, all roads would appear in fact to lead to that equally familiar alternative destination of Ruin.

Whilst I confess not to being inclined to superstition, recent events having taken their inevitable toll, it is all I can do to resist the temptation to keep my fingers perpetually crossed. The much maligned eczema rash which haunts the index and middle fingers of both hands has proved my saving grace in this respect. Such friction as would be caused by the action of their crossing (in the shameful service of superstition) would result in a discomfort that far outweighs any hoped for protection that the supposed forces of fate could afford me.

Had I but realised what lay before us when I gave Colonel Braithwaite full command of the Harvest Festival Preparations Committee, then the ensuing disaster could have been well and truly prevented. Hindsight not being on the menu that particular day, things remained in primed-for-disaster mode.

St. Cliff's, being in a rural location, is well endowed when it comes to members of the farming community, and it has been our happy task (until now), to appoint a representative from these veritable tillers of the soil to oversee our harvest proceedings.

Colonel Braithwaite, whilst having only farmed for two years, produced a crop of wheat sporting ears that would have kept Goliath in Weetabix for life. I can only presume that my willingness to be impressed got the better of me and, whilst I was more than prepared to accept the good Colonel's explanation of 'beginner's luck', an air of suspicion hung heavily over the rest of the village.

Their worst fears had to wait until the unfortunate day of St. Cliff's Harvest Festival to receive official confirmation.

Never in living memory had such gargantuan crops adorned the sanctuary of St. Cliff's, and one's imagination needed little assistance to picture what the Garden of Eden must have looked like in all its pre-fall splendour.

On this particular day, the opportunity to linger upon such wistful thoughts was rudely interrupted, not only by a duff first chord from Mrs Higginbottom as she attempted to kick-start the congregation into 'We plough the fields and scatter', but also by the half dozen men from the Ministry of Agriculture who, dressed to the nines in chemical warfare-style apparel, launched forth to the front of the church and proceeded to dismantle Colonel Braithwaite's super-sized offerings and bag them for analysis.

The undisguised smirks that adorned the ruddy faces of his farming competitors were all that was required to establish precisely who it was had given the tip-off that genetically modified crops were being illegally grown in the parish.

It now falls upon me to break the news to St. Cliff's Harvest Supper Committee that Whopper Jacket Potatoes are most definitely off the menu tonight.

Onward and upward
Derek

The age of miracles!
5 October, 2010

Dear Friends

Life at St. Cliff's can be rather all-consuming, and thus the opportunity to 'chill out' (as I understand it is referred to in contemporary parlance) and relax with a good book in the all-encompassing leathery sumptuousness of our recently acquired 'La-z-boy Manual Recliner' (not that I would wish to lay claim to the tardiness alluded to in its overly-hyphenated branding), is a pleasure much treasured by this humble clergyman.

Of late I have enjoyed reading about the life of that famed man of God, Smith Wigglesworth no less.

It must be said that there are not many ministers of the cloth who could get away with walloping prayer line clientele whilst still achieving such good results along the way.

I will confess that on one occasion, I myself had to resist the temptation to follow in Mr Wigglesworth's pugilistic footsteps. However, this had absolutely nothing pertaining to the hoped for efficacy of a miraculous healing and everything to do with old Mr McMurtry (an age-old regular at St. Cliff's) and his extremely annoying habit of finding the smallest pin prick of a hole in my theological reasoning, then attempting to drive the coach and horses of his well-honed opinions right through it.

That is by the by.

I refer to Mr Wigglesworth because it has long been my desire to see the fires of Pentecost ablaze within this fair parish, and not to be just the reserve of the like of that great man of yore.

Emboldened by the consumption of two whole chapters of the aforementioned book, I resolved that I would likewise seek out worthy candidates for a miraculous healing.

The need to travel into town to purchase a fresh supply of correcting fluid (the writing of my sermon for this Sunday being a little more angst-ridden than I had hoped for) provided just the ready opportunity I was looking for to 'go into all the world'.

Having decided upon availing myself of public transport to reduce my carbon footprint (and, I shamefully admit, the number of parking tickets I seem prone to attracting), I waited with much faith-filled anticipation at the bus stop as the number 57 turned the corner and pulled up to collect my good self.

As I gingerly traversed the packed bus in search of a seat whilst it lurched forward at great speed (no doubt in a bid to make up for lost time, it being, by my reckoning, a good ten minutes overdue), I could not help but notice a parishioner of mine, Mrs Greengrass, perched in an aisle seat and sporting a walking stick.

Our paths having crossed on many a prayer line in the pursuit of ridding the afflicted pensioner of a persistent in-growing toenail, I (feeling a pang of guilt that the lady had not, as yet, been freed from her ailment by my intervention) summoned up from within myself as much Smith Wigglesworth-like faith as I could muster, and proceeded to command the lady to stand to her feet.

At this point I had in my mind also the image of Peter outside the Gate Beautiful, commanding the crippled beggar to rise from his infirmity, but the words that proceeded from my lips lacked the eloquence of the esteemed apostle.

Instead I simply told the somewhat stunned Mrs Greengrass to, 'Get out of your seat, woman!'

That I had intended this to be by way of her receiving the provision of a miraculous healing appeared lost on my fellow travellers and, for that matter, the bus driver. Slamming his foot on the brakes, he strode down the vehicle and frog-marched me to the now open rear door, through which he forcibly thrust me from the bus.

A defence of my actions was futile and I had to suffer not only the ignominy of the doors closing shut in my face, but also the stern-faced glares of the other passengers before whom I stood accused of that second most heinous of travellers' crimes, namely, taking the seat of an old person (the first being that of taking the seat of a pregnant woman).

Perhaps I should count myself fortunate that my eyes did not settle on young Clarissa Thompson, whose face raced past me as the bus shot away at speed. That she is seven months pregnant, who knows what terrible outcome would have awaited me had I launched forth in similar manner, and addressed her sprained ankle instead?

Onward and upward
Derek

Derek just couldn't seem to take the bell ringing seriously!

Dear Friends

Having long supplemented my daily bowl of fortified, own brand breakfast cereal (I have probably mentioned the challenges of a clergyman's stipend on more than one occasion) with not only a spoonful of sugar but also the digesting of a variety of helpful Bible reading notes, in a moment of oat-fuelled madness, I decided to have a go at jolly well writing some Bible notes of my own in a bid to feed my oft malnourished flock at St. Cliff's on a daily basis.

When I allude to their famished state, I assure you that it is not for the want of trying.

Whilst regularly serving up an ample supply of God's Word on a weekly basis to aid their spiritual growth (with the odd exception of the occasional duff visiting speaker – I have made a particular mental note not to invite the self-appointed Apostle Smith again; that he was quickly renamed Apostate Smith by my congregation did not bode well for him), I fear that I may yet have my work cut out if they are to be in with even half a chance of appearing in any proposed sequel to the Hebrews 'hall of fame'.

For your edification, I have copied a sample portion of my profferings on the St. Cliff's antiquated photocopier but, by the looks of it, my meagre reproductive skills combined with its limited printing capabilities have perhaps not delivered the 'pukka' result I might have wished for.

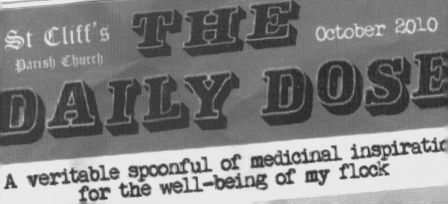

St Cliff's Parish Church — THE — October 2010

DAILY DOSE

A veritable spoonful of medicinal inspiration for the well-being of my flock

Wednesday 13th October

What an example to us all is that chap in the familiar Bible story of 'The Good Samaritan'. A poor traveller on his uppers because of nasty ne'er-do-wells and then, just in the nick of time, a kind fellow crosses the road to bring him much needed succour and sustenance.

But today I do not intend to focus on the sorry circumstances of this unfortunate tale. In that the intended purpose of 'The Daily Dose' is to deliver those in my charge a veritable antidote to the ills of life, allow me instead to recount a little joke of my creation (laughter is, after all, the best medicine) that this particular Bible story inspired.

Gentleman: 'Why did the chicken cross the road?'

Lady: 'I have not the slightest idea. Pray tell me, kind sir, why?'

Gentleman: 'Aha! The question, good lady, is not so much why the chicken crossed the road but what in fact it was doing in the story of The Good Samaritan in the first place.'

Onward and upward

Derek

'Post Scriptum. The more observant among you will note that I have plagarised this joke from a previous missive. I fear that my repertoire of but one 'gag' does not bode well for my entry into St. Cliff's Exorcism Committee's comedic fundraising event, 'Stand-Up and Deliver'.

Thursday 14th October

The lot of a clergyman, it must be said, necessitates taking the rough with the smooth, and with that in mind, I am forced to empathise with the prophet Elisha and those insolent youths who mocked his unfortunate bald pate.

My gentle stroll through the village today was interrupted by the uncalled for taunts of a group of youths who were loitering outside Fags and Mags (our local purveyor of confectionery, periodicals and, of course, the aforementioned 'fags'). The proprietor's policy of limiting to three the number of adolescents entering his establishment at one time (the mysterious disappearance of various popular chocolate snacks being ample justification for his draconian stance) inevitably resulted in a backlog of teenage clientele awaiting entrance outside.

It would not be the first time that I have been referred to as 'Rev', 'Bish', 'The Pope', and other such pejorative epithets, but it was certainly the first time that my less-than-luxuriant scalp had been the focus of a cutting jibe by these queuing youngsters.

That the purpose of my visit to the commercial centre of the village was to purchase a hair-reviving product simply added salt to the wound.

Before I had the opportunity to consider my response to their rather hurtful remark, the offending youths were set upon by a passing Great Dane, who appeared to have a penchant for the particular brand of spicy potato crisps that one of the group was eating.

Whilst their fate might not have been quite so final as that of Elisha's taunters at the hands (or should I say, paws) of the marauding beast who secured their untimely demise (a slobbery packet of crisps being the extent of the punishment meted out to these caustic offenders), I am nevertheless inclined to err on the side of grace and to let bygones be bygones. This will, I trust, put to bed the conflicting nagging notion that perhaps, on this occasion, vengeance was indeed the Lord's.

Onward and upward
Derek

Friday 15th October

I love a good film and a favourite of mine is *Apollo 13*.
I enjoyed it thoroughly, even though I had not seen the previous twelve in the series (a little joke of mine to lighten the load).

How stirring a scene is that of our heroes' attempted return to earth, one fellow keeping the horizontal axis of the ailing craft steady and another the vertical, in a desperate bid not to miss their target (assuredly an analogy of faith as we fix our sights on the prize) and shoot back off into outer space, never to return. That unfortunate outcome would have been sad indeed, because I for one have always particularly enjoyed Tom Hanks, and the film world would have been the poorer without him had that happened.

Fortunately for us all, it did not.

Which leads me to my thought for this day that life, dear friends, is like a space craft, not literally of

Across the pond!

20 October, 2010

Dear Friends

It has often been an accusation thrust my way that I have a tendency to be a little naive when it comes to the ways of the world.

This tenet was proved true only the other day when my good lady wife, having without doubt sneakily taken the liberty to examine the healthy (and ever-increasing) membership of my 'online' congregation, pointed out that I appeared to have attracted a considerable number of friends from 'across the pond'.

Not being completely au fait with modern parlance, I assumed that she was referring to the residents of Twilight Villas, the retirement home which stands imposingly at the opposite side of the stagnant and lifeless pool of water at the centre of our village.

I could not quite believe my good fortune that, having traversed the 'Worldwide Super Highway' in pursuit of what I gather are known as 'cyber' friendships, lo and behold, I had those among this number residing within my own fair parish, but a stone's throw from the manse!

Such was my excitement at this epiphany that, although it was late in the evening, I sallied forth immediately to make myself known to them.

Feeling that this joyous occasion did not merit my usual British reserve, I knocked on the front door of the retirement home with such gusto that you could have been forgiven for thinking that I was intending to break into the property forcibly.

In a matter of moments, heads popped out of windows.

I do not know quite what came over me next (put it down to my temporary exuberance) but, throwing caution to the wind, I blurted out loudly that if they opened the front door I had a treat in store for them, meaning our connection on the World Wide Super Highway.

What I was unaware of was that the frail and timid folk at Twilight Villas had recently been warned not to open their door to strangers on the occasion of the looming Halloween festivities. This would not have been a problem had not one of their number been a little heavy-handed in turning over the pages of their communal calendar, and thus unfortunately skipping over two full weeks. I say, unfortunately, because as far as the elderly residents were concerned, the night I had chosen to call round, unannounced, was indeed the feared 31st of October, that night of unwanted and oft ghoulish visitors.

It was only when two gentlemen from the local constabulary arrived to ask for an explanation of my anti-social behaviour and why I had been intimidating the folk from the old people's home, that it began to dawn on me that perhaps there had been a crossed wire or two along the way.

That I had chosen to wear my black cape as a guard against the chill night air only increased the suspicions of these officers of the law that I was garbed as that fanged gentleman of cinematic fame and not as a man of the cloth, as I repeatedly (and unsuccessfully) tried to persuade them.

Having returned to the manse under the cloud of their somewhat threat-laden warning that they 'would be keeping an eye on me', I then discovered from my wife that I had got the wrong end of the proverbial stick (as usual) and that she was in fact referring to folk from the United States of America.

Whilst I do offer a heartfelt welcome to our distant cousins, it is probably best that I restrict any future communication with your good selves to the medium of the internet.

I have assuredly had my fill of pastoral visits to my 'online' congregation for quite some time.

Onward and upward
Derek

Must reschedule our 'Spirit Come!' revival meeting on 31st October. Probably inadvisable that it falls on Halloween!

The final countdown!
27 October, 2010
Dear Friends

I am presently filled with unabated excitement as we, and by that I mean the good folk at St. Cliff's, eagerly await the arrival of our first full-time youth worker.

If you have followed my 'blogs' through the months of August and September, you will be well aware of the dearth of suitable candidates responding to my eye-catching, quarter page advertisement in *World of Anglicanism*.

If it had not been for the timely receipt of an application from a young lady called Millie (although I am now informed that she was in fact christened, Emily, which has caused me not a little confusion as to where to place her within my alphabetically ordered address book), I would have had to go, cap in hand, to Mr Clench, our overly cautious (and unfortunately named) treasurer, for the requisite funds to re-publish the advertisement for a second costly month.

My reluctance to do this might perhaps have been lessened had I not recently been upbraided for running up what he considered to be an excessive bill for the purchase of two dozen boxes of man-sized Kleenex tissues (our prayer ministry team would appear to be on a bit of a roll at present).

Fortunately for me, I was spared this ignominious fate and, with the spring back in my step, I am now counting down the days until the beginning of the month when 'Millie' begins her tenure.

I count my blessings that I do not have to rely upon my scant knowledge of the mores of young people to facilitate her smooth passage into this newly created position. Between you and me, I have leaned rather heavily of late on the expertise of Mrs Bracegirdle, the mainstay of our local Christian bookshop, to advise me as to some youth-orientated resources to add to our sample copy of *Youth Work* magazine.

Because her previous realm of employ was at a charity shop frequented by cash-strapped teenagers, she would thus appear to have her finger squarely on the pulse of the 'up-to-date' trends.

It is directly as a result of her informed counsel that I have purchased (out of my own pocket, for previously mentioned reasons) a video of something called *Veggie Tales*, an ample supply of colourful WWJD wristbands, which I gather are all the rage at the moment (although Mrs Bracegirdle was at a loss to tell me what indeed these enigmatic initials actually stand for), six illustrated copies of the Good News Bible (pictures are a must for youngsters it would appear), and something called Flannelgraph, which she assures me will aid the communication of all things biblical to 'Millie's' future charges.

This last purchase was perhaps a tad more pricey than I had expected, and I will do my best to quell any suspicions that Mrs Bracegirdle has 'got one over on me' in the pursuit of some extra commission to supplement her meagre wage.

All things considered, I remain in an upbeat mood and am sure that the outlay will be worth it simply to see the expression on the face of young 'Millie' when she joins us next week.

I cannot but wait.

Onward and upward
Derek

That's the televangelist in
Derek coming out again!

Nov

10

Ghoul hash!

5 November, 2010

Dear Friends

It would appear that I am at present suffering from a decidedly irritating condition affecting my feet that even the most eminent of chiropodists would find themselves stretched to the limits of their capabilities attempting to remedy. Namely, whenever a situation presents itself through which I might achieve some brief moment of glory, as surely as night follows day I can be guaranteed to well and truly 'put my foot in it'.

The opportunity to present a creative alternative to Halloween was uppermost in the minds of St. Cliff's Evangelism Committee when they proposed the tenuously titled, Hallo-lujah-een Party, not least in a thinly veiled attempt to keep all potential trick and treating pranksters and egg throwers within the confines of the building (rather than outside like last year where they 'omeletted' the front porch with enough eggs to give a vegan apoplexy. This situation was exacerbated by the surprisingly unseasonable tropical heat wave that visited the parish the very next morning and gave new meaning to the expression 'high church'.)

The lure of copious supplies of free food and Marvo – 'it's not magic, it's just an illusion' – the Christian conjuror, did the trick, so to speak, and there probably wasn't a home in the locale that wasn't devoid of offspring for that particular evening.

I can only put what happened next down to the frivolous party atmosphere that filled St. Cliff's and, with all things going smoothly, I mischievously took my leave to play a prank on Mrs Willoughby who was, or so I thought, engaged in her weekly clean of the crypt.

Donning a somewhat ghoulish mask that I had confiscated from young Jason Potter, who had planned to appear as a deformed shepherd in last year's nativity, I hid behind a tombstone and prepared to pounce.

I did not have long to wait.

Footsteps on the stony floor were my signal and, with much ghostly relish, I leapt to my feet with a wail that would have caused the infamous hound of the Baskervilles to turn tail.

If only it had been a dog that I had frightened the socks off, or even Mrs Willoughby.

Sadly it was neither.

Had I but had even the faintest inkling that the verger would take it upon himself to give the assembled children a whirlwind tour of St. Cliff's while Marvo went to look for his missing white rabbit, then I would have pulled the plug on my ghoulish enterprise post-haste.

This was not to be and I now fear that I will have to use the forthcoming Remembrance Day service to try to make my own peace with the parents of these traumatised youngsters.

Onward and upward
Derek

Where two or three are gathered!
14 November, 2010
Dear Friends

You will be pleased to hear that young Millie, our full-time youth worker, is now fully ensconced within the confines of St. Cliff's.

It seemed most fitting that we threw caution to the wind and made a big splash to welcome her amongst us.

Having persuaded St. Cliff's Catering Committee to shelve their suggestion of a 'faith tea' (in that this 'spiritual-sounding' option is suggested far too frequently for my liking I suspect an element of laziness is creeping into their indomitable ranks), a compromise was found and it was agreed to send out for that fail-safe staple of the British diet, namely, fish and chips.

I say compromise, because I have a strong suspicion that the aforementioned Catering Committee are still adhering to a 'work to rule' in protest at being asked to add hot chocolate to the post-service drinks menu, with particular reference to the difficulties involved in removing the sticky dregs of this wintry beverage from St. Cliff's antique crockery.

Having been rather preoccupied with ensuring that young Millie's entrée into St. Cliff's went without a proverbial hitch, I gave little consideration as to what else might potentially clash with this eagerly anticipated occasion.

That the manse television has been out of action since we rather foolishly allowed our miniscule youth group to utilise it in the services of something called a 'Wii', which resulted in its accompanying handset flying headlong into the screen (and rendering it inoperative), I have thus been completely oblivious to the fact that our planned 'social' was not the only attraction available to the faithful of St. Cliff's on a Saturday evening.

It is a blessing indeed that Millie has such an easy-going disposition and did not take it as a personal slight that a mere seven of our congregation (who, I would hazard, had a combined age that all but matched that of Methuselah) turned up to bid her welcome. If I had known that the *X-Factor* (a popular talent show, I gather) held the nation in its thrall, then perhaps I could have opted for an earlier commencement of the proceedings.

I will admit to feeling a little embarrassed that the large order we had promised our local purveyors of fish and chips (and which I had humorously suggested would be akin to that famous biblical haul miraculously gifted to Jesus' disciples by their Master) instead bore a much closer resemblance to the proffering of the young lad in that other biblical story of the feeding of the five thousand.

Having decided to proceed with the evening as planned, it did not go unnoticed that young Millie appeared to spend most of the time on her mobile telephone (though I believe she persisted in referring to it as a Blackcurrant or some such).

Whilst accepting her defence that she was 'texting' the young folk of St. Cliff's to keep them abreast of the contents of my well-honed welcome speech, I am now beginning to suspect that these telephonic messages had, in fact, more to do with finding out how certain contestants on this talent show were doing.

There is obviously more to young Millie than meets the eye, and perhaps it is high time that I availed myself of a new mobile telephone of this modern ilk if I intend to keep our new youth worker within my sights.

Then again, maybe it would be wise to hold fire for a bit. I fear that our treasurer will first need to recover from the news that I will unfortunately have to bring him that we have lost our non-refundable deposit of £100 (in anticipation of a bumper order) to the fish and chip shop.

Onward and upward
Derek

A second crack of the whip!
24 November, 2010
Dear Friends

Christmas looms large and we are once again looking forward with eager anticipation to that ever-popular feature on our church calendar, namely, 'Carols at St. Cliff's'.

Last year, in a bid to pep things up a little, I invited my flock to vote for their favourite Christmas carol, with the winner to be announced at the aforementioned festive occasion.

Probably as a result of over-indulging in too many pre-service mince pies (which we later discovered had been laced with enough brandy to incinerate a sizeable Christmas pudding), the bishop gamely offered to link his carol service epilogue with the winning carol.

I can only think that, moving within ecclesiastical circles (as we both do), it had not occurred to either of us that the general populace nowadays considers the simple inclusion of the sound of sleigh bells, or a passing reference to Santa Claus, enough to guarantee a seasonal song inclusion within the canon of that which passes for a carol.

It was therefore not only somewhat embarrassing for the bishop to have to announce that the winning entry was a ditty entitled, 'All I Want for Christmas is You', but the situation was exacerbated by the unwanted attentions of old Miss Wiggins, who for some time has made her affections towards the bishop more than clear.

That she happened to be sitting but three feet from the bishop's gaze did not help matters in the least and, whilst he valiantly attempted to connect this popular song with the newborn babe in a manger, the infatuated woman remained unconvinced, assuming it to be singularly directed at her.

The bishop has graciously (though with a little trepidation) accepted my invitation for a 'second crack of the whip' at this year's festive evening, but I have clearly stipulated to one and all that all nominations must carry a biblical theme.

Having once more presented my congregation with the opportunity to partake in the voting process, I have been left with a nagging doubt that there might lurk a song of the masses which meets my criteria, but which might yet leave the bishop once again exposed.

Onward and upward
Derek

Once bitten!
2 December, 2010

Dear Friends

Much is made of the community spirit that manifests itself at times such as these, and in this I refer to the present deluge of snow that has befallen this fair land.

Having ventured forth from the warmth and comfort of the manse (forsaking my emergency supply of chocolate digestives) to assist in the clearing of St. Cliff's front path, it did not occur to me that I might lay myself open to the opportunistic high spirits of our youth group whilst engaged in my good deed.

Being unfamiliar with the 'text' facility on my mobile phone, I was unaware that Millie, our newly installed youth worker, had organised an impromptu snowball fight within the grounds of St. Cliff's.

Perhaps I should have removed my clerical vestments prior to going out, but old habits die hard. Having gamely laughed off a 'direct hit' from young Charlie Wiggins, which necessitated the hasty removal of my sodden dog collar to retrieve the remains of the frozen missile from my person, I would have done well to adopt that helpful maxim of, 'once bitten, twice shy'.

The fact that I did not, simply laid me open to further calamity.

I naively agreed to the culprit's offer to make a snow angel by way of apology. That St. Cliff's might yet have a seasonal sculpture to outdo that of the Methodists and their snowy monstrosity, which purported to be an accurate rendition of John Wesley while boasting a carrot for its nose, cheered me no end.

Had I but known that a snow angel required the services of the human form lying flat in the icy drifts, then perhaps I might have been a little more alert.

I was not.

I have a strong suspicion that it was not only the hand of Master Wiggins that floored me, but also the outstretched floral wellington boot of Millie.

It is now not only my dog collar that will need to reside over-night in our already clogged-up airing cupboard, but almost every garment I was wearing.

Whilst it would appear that all concerned consider me to be a 'good sport' and that our new youth worker seems to have built a rapport with her charges, I cannot help but feel that it has been at my expense.

Fortunately, I am preaching on the subject of grace this coming Sunday and I trust that this will help me to overcome the temptation with which I am wrestling – namely, to turn off the heating in the youth room during the service to give them a taste of their own medicine.

Onward and upward
Derek

Dear Friends

Having recently enjoyed a 'movie night' at the manse with my good lady wife (a dvd having been procured for the occasion from our local video rental establishment, one of the selling features being a behind-the-scenes look at how the popular film was made), I hit upon the idea of treating my 'online' flock to what a page of one of my sermons might look like, before it was premiered, so to speak.

Whilst it might not be quite as exciting as an explanation of how the stunts on *Free Willy 2* are performed (this being our chosen dvd, a particular favourite of mine), I am hoping that a little glimpse into how one of my sermons is crafted will at the least be of some interest.

Onward and upward
Derek

...nd I can wholeheartedly empathise with the calamity that faced Mary and Joseph as they entered the little town of Bethlehem on that very first Christmas.

(pause)

A minister's stipend being what it is invariably limits the choice that my good lady wife and I have when it comes to considering the partaking of a break from the rigours of ministry.
Had it not been for the unexpected fiscal outlay in the services of replacing the recently defunct manse washing machine (a Hotpoint WML760P Aquarius 1600 Spin Washing Machine in white being our preferred choice) things might have been altogether different.
That we purchased this unwanted (but assuredly necessary) electrical appliance from an outlet of a Tesco Direct emporium ensured the collection of enough 'Clubcard' loyalty points to tip the balance in our favour and ensure their redemption as a weekend break for two in a Travelodge establishment of our choice, no less.

Our Nissan Micra being 'out of action' due ^to its inability to cope with the arctic conditions presently assailing our fair land we availed ourself of public transport to convey us to our selected destination. That we are neither of us good travellers when it comes to this communal mode of transport we settled on a Travelodge in the locale, but a short ten minute bus ride (including stops).

Such close proximity would not ordinarily have been a problem but for the fact that on that fated day the duty receptionist happened to be none other than Frank Peacock a rather argumentative fellow who, having taken liberties with the ample dregs of the communion wine one Sunday at St Cliff's proceeded (in his intoxicated state) to persistently interrupt the flow of my sermon.

Oops! No apostrophe!!!

It's pithy title of 'Expel the immoral brother' was pure coincidence.
Having had the inebriated fellow summarily removed from the building I thought that this would be the end of the matter.
Sadly, this was not the case.

Whilst Frank Peacock's senses might have been more than a little dulled on the aforementioned occasion, on the day of our arrival they were more than sharp enough for him to immediately recognise my clerical visage as he looked up from his examination of that day's bookings.

← will folk know what visage means?

To give him credit the fellow did not even skip a beat as he smugly delivered, with perfect irony, those immortal and festal words, "Sorry Reverend. No room in the inn".

at

I can only assume that the force with which he then slammed the bookings roster shut was the cause of our 'Anytime Return' bus tickets (which I had temporarily placed on the counter) being forcibly blown to goodness knows where thus compounding the embarrassing situation.

Unlike the parents of the Christmas babe my good lady wife and myself did not find alternative lodging and thus had to return home, on foot. *!!!*

* Remove from membership!

'Tis the season to be jolly!
22 December, 2010

Dear Friends

Another year has almost passed and once again the season of goodwill toward all men is upon us. Whilst this goodwill may be proceeding bountifully to us from a heavenward direction, its horizontal progress, man to man, is, I have to say, more than a tad stop start.

In time-honoured fashion, we at St. Cliff's had willingly embraced the spirit of ecumenism and were more than happy to do our bit by joining with our brothers and sisters from the other churches in the parish to leaflet drop the village, as to the times and occasions of the many and various Christmas services that will inevitably be taking place.

Must remember to vet songs for Sunday's nativity. Last year's 'Mary, Mary, quite contrary' must on no account be repeated!

I have to confess that it was all a bit 'last minute' for my liking, and the first sight any of us had of the said leaflet was but seconds before commencement. Thus its content was something we had to trust to its producers, a decision we were later to regret.

Had it not been for an invitation to partake of mince pies and hot drinking chocolate at the home of old Mrs Williams, we would not have had the opportunity to peruse the missive that we had been dutifully delivering.

Even by the light of Mrs Williams' rather annoying, randomly flashing Christmas tree lights, it was still possible to make out the variations in print quality which blatantly emphasised the offerings of one particular church over all the other faintly printed ones, St. Cliff's being among their number.

It would not have required the services of Sherlock Holmes to work out to which church Mr Stannard, the printer of this ephemeral document, was affiliated.

As if this wasn't enough, it would now seem that a veritable ecumenical war has broken out as a direct result of this underhand ploy to cream off the Christmas trade, with all but our good selves now vigorously engaged in canvassing the parish to promote their particular denominational Christmas offerings.

I have noticed that even Mr Cone, the ice cream man, who I will admit does have a rather lean time of it during the winter season, has been employed in this unseemly fracas, with his speaker system being used to announce (in strict rotation with his theme tune of 'Popeye the Sailor Man') which is the best church to go to this Christmas!

Such is life, but we at St. Cliff's have decided upon what we consider to be the most obvious of enticements.

I think that perhaps we will simply preach about God breaking into history as a baby, growing up to be a man and dying on behalf of sinful man. That, I suspect, will be sufficient.

Let us now simply fervently pray that Mrs Higginbottom, our erratic organist, saves that bottle of Harvey's Bristol Cream I bought her as an early Christmas gift until after 'Carols at St. Cliff's', in the vain hope that she may yet pull off a rendition of 'Silent Night' that isn't the volume it was last year. Such was the din, I feared she would not only awaken the Christmas babe from his slumbers, but probably most of the residents of St. Cliff's graveyard to boot!

With my best wishes to you this Christmas,

Onward and upward
Derek

Derek's really got into the spirit of Christmas this year!

A new year begins!
6 January, 2011
Dear Friends

A new year begins and this, I am certain, is going to be St. Cliff's year. I can feel it in my water. Which reminds me, I must make a point of removing my emergency supply of effervescent Alka Seltzer tablets from my trouser pocket when called upon to conduct baptisms.

When Mrs Philpott sprang back to new life from the tepid depths of St. Cliff's baptistry last month, she all but cleared the first two rows of the congregation who feared that, having been buried to her old life, she had now risen up, foaming at the mouth, as the first of a new breed of rabid believers.

I have taken it upon myself to write to the chairman of the pharmaceutical company responsible, suggesting that perhaps a little less fizz in their product would be no bad thing.

Every cloud has a silver lining and Mrs Philpott assures me that since that unfortunate day, she hasn't suffered half as much from indigestion as she used to. A blessing indeed!

With the festive season but a fading memory, I have taken it upon myself to propose to the Christmas Decorations Committee that it would perhaps be in everyone's interest if next year we purchase either an artificial tree or one that has not the least hint of a root. Notwithstanding, that is, the rather vociferous objections from old Mr McMurtry, that allowing a Christmas tree into St. Cliff's is tantamount to heresy being that, 'there be no mention of them there pagan abominations in the Holy Scriptures'.

In that the Bible is somewhat silent on the subject of Christmas cards also, I feel duty bound to scrub Mr McMurtry from my Christmas card list post-haste lest I be accused of straying into heresy in this matter too.

With regard to the said Christmas tree, whilst I recognise

that Mrs Roberts' flower ladies were more than keen to use up the somewhat excessive 'job lot' of Baby Bio that came their way courtesy of Mr Roberts (and no doubt the rear end of a lorry at some point, if I know her husband), their daily routine of generous plant food top-ups for our tree only served to encourage the already over-sized tinsel tower that the Christmas Decorations Committee had seen fit to inflict upon us, to sprout heavenward at a rate of knots that would have put any Apollo rocket launch to shame. Thus it left us with not only a superlative hole in the roof, but also as the only church in the parish that could boast a 'spire' at both ends, one of which sported the slightly more garish crowning glory of an intermittently flashing Christmas fairy.

One can only hope that when the bishop joined us for 'Carol's at St. Cliff's', his perennial neck ailment kept his gaze fixed firmly earthbound.

We can but wonder what this year has in store for us at St. Cliff's.

Onward and upward
Derek

As far as Derek is concerned,
a day of rest is a day of rest!

Out of the frying pan!
20 January, 2011
Dear Friends

It has long been my desire to 'up my game' at St. Cliff's, and recently chancing upon the biblical account of Daniel's fast at the court of King Nebuchadnezzar, I settled upon a similar course of action for my congregation.

That the nearest my flock had come to this particular spiritual discipline was on the occasion of one of our ubiquitous 'faith teas' (a round of banana sandwiches which had most certainly seen better days being the only proffering on which the fifty or so hungry folk were expected to gorge themselves), did nothing to make me reconsider.

I put my lack of faith to multiply these 'loaves and fishes' squarely down to my not wishing to see the dubious-looking things replicated. That is my excuse and I am sticking to it! The fact that I had saved the assembled throng from having to digest the blackened and soggy snack was quickly forgotten as stomachs began to rumble.

Sadly, our organist Mrs Higginbottom's valiant attempt to take their minds off the increasing pangs of hunger with her party piece, 'Food Glorious Food' (from the popular musical *Oliver*), only added to the collective sense of dissatisfaction.

My suggestion to the disgruntled assembly that we should perhaps turn it into an impromptu time of prayer and fasting was unfortunately drowned out by some faithless wag proposing that we all pop down to our local purveyor of fish and chips at once. It was, he shockingly suggested, probably what the disciples (in the aforementioned story) did anyway. My attempt to halt the subsequent mass exodus on the basis that St. Cliff's was presently considering boycotting The Piece of Cod because of its irreverent name, fell on deaf ears.

In the light of these events, I fear that I have made a rod for my own back and, in my enthusiasm to press ahead with my proposed fast, I asked Mr Graham (the entrenched editor of St. Cliff's monthly magazine, *Onward and Upward*) to include its date in our February issue.

I will shamefully confess that my rationale for selecting the evening of 8th March was that my good lady wife and I had a pending dinner invitation at the home of Mr and Mrs Bidmarsh. Having once previously endured an entire coffee and dessert evening with them, the greater part of which was spent protecting a piece of lemon meringue pie from their slavering Rottweiler, I was certainly in no hurry to revisit the scene of the crime so soon.

It seemed as worthy an excuse as I could muster to schedule in the fast on this very day, and thus save ourselves another such torturous evening.

I now discover that the date I have plumped for is in fact Shrove Tuesday, that day of pancake over-indulgence! If I was a superstitious man, I would say that my duplicity with respect to Mr and Mrs Bidmarsh has come back to haunt me. That I am not doesn't seem to put me any more at ease.

Whilst I have it on good authority that Mr Graham will not be purloining the services of St. Cliff's trusty photocopier until two days hence, I have been curtly informed by him that the forthcoming issue has, to all intents and purposes, 'gone to press' and that no further changes can now be made, vicar or not.

How my congregation will take the news of the fast when they open their copy of the magazine, I dare not surmise.

With Shrove Tuesday looming large, this is indeed a case of 'out of the frying pan and into the fire'.

Onward and upward
Derek

St. Cliff's
— Parish Church —

25th January, 2011
Dear Mr Philpott

My heartfelt thanks for stepping into the breach on the occasion of our treasurer being absent last Sunday morning, and agreeing to count St. Cliff's Sunday offering. I sincerely hope that the miscreant who mischievously stole his hairpiece on the number 49 bus the previous day returns it promptly so that his dignity is once more restored.

Having said that, I will confess that some Sundays, counting the offering is sadly not a taxing job and I cannot escape the feeling that God is getting tipped rather than given to.

Which leads me on rather nicely to your recent email enquiring as to remuneration for your 'accountancy' services.

I prefer to view our labours for the Kingdom as having their motivation primarily in our hearts and not in our bank balance, and thus would like to take this opportunity to clarify that indeed the 'great commission' (as mentioned in the Bible) is not 10%, which you point out is presently the going rate at your regular place of employ as a waiter at 'The Leaning Tower of Pizza'.

With that matter cleared up, I trust that we can still count on your services in future if we are ever 'down a man', though hopefully next time not at our unfortunate treasurer's expense.

Perhaps, in the light of your professional experience, you would also be best redeployed in another area of church life such as the serving of communion. If this is the case, may I swiftly add that when serving the wine, please note that the option of red or white is not one that this particular establishment can offer.

Yours sincerely

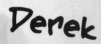

Derek

A small request!
7 February, 2011
Dear Friends

I note with great excitement and anticipation that, come 5th March (just under a month hence), my regular 'blogospherical' missives will be celebrating their first anniversary.

Whilst I have an idea brewing as to how to reward my 'online' flock on this occasion (I believe that within media circles such information would be classed as a 'teaser'), I would ask that you be so kind as to invite your friends to join us.

To those who have already been faithful promoters of my output, your efforts have been much appreciated. Although I cannot guarantee you a reward in heaven for your valiant services to 'the cause', I am considering making available a copy of Mrs Parsley-Smythe's prized, and somewhat controversial, rock cake recipe (there are as yet unfounded rumours that they owe a little of their resilience to a pinch of cement dust) by way of thanks.

That this joyous anniversary coincides with one of my monthly meetings with the bishop is, I confess, a tad behind my motivation. It was he, after all, who rather ridiculed my dalliance with the world of 'blogging' in the first place, and it would assuredly be a feather in this clergyman's cap if I were to prove him wrong.

All I have to do now is assuage this nagging doubt that perhaps making such a point isn't quite the done thing for a man in my position.

Onward and upward
Derek

A moment of madness!
11 February, 2011
Dear Friends

I believe that an apology is in order in that my initial prolific output onto the now familiar 'blogosphere' has somewhat dwindled of late. Not greatly, I hasten to add, but I haven't 'blogged' perhaps as frequently as I would have hoped to.

Before you come down too hard on me, I think I am justified in laying claim to the worthy excuse of 'mitigating circumstances'. My defence is that the pastoral pressures of shepherding the faithful at St. Cliff's have rather got on top of me of late, and were compounded by my quite foolish (with hindsight) and extensive list of new year's resolutions.

Such was its length that resolves like: 1) Avoid getting overly stressed; 2) Take more time to relax; 3) Cast my cares on God; 4) Do not worry what you will eat or drink for tomorrow has enough worries of its own (and many more besides), simply added to the list of demands upon me, and thus became burdens to fulfil in and of themselves.

It was this that led me, in a moment of stress-induced madness, to 'Google' (as I believe this popular World Wide Web search function is called) for 'online' sermons to free me from this all-pervading tyranny.

What good fortune (or so I thought) that I should accidentally hit the 'I'm feeling lucky' option with my errant and unreliable mouse (its purchase from a gentleman purporting to be a bona fide computer reseller in the market was assuredly a mistake, I now see) and strike gold immediately.

A ready-made sermon based upon Deuteronomy chapter 28, snappily entitled, 'Blessed is Best! Cursed is Worst!', with a guaranteed maximum delivery time of thirty minutes (I know all too well the limited capacity of my congregation at St. Cliff's) seemed too good to pass up.

That I was already planning to preach from Deuteronomy 28 on its catalogue of glorious blessings and gruesome curses presented by God to the Israelites was sufficient enough to persuade me to print the thing at once in readiness for the ensuing Sunday morning service.

I am not a man inclined to superstition, but the subsequent recurrence of my age-old eczema rash, which has revisited (with a vengeance) the index and middle fingers of my right hand since the delivery of this 'borrowed' sermon, has made me feel uneasy to say the least. It is verse 27 of the passage which, in particular, seems to have been sent to taunt me: 'The LORD will afflict you with the boils of Egypt and with tumours, festering sores and the itch, from which you cannot be cured.'

Whilst I fully believe in the truth that, as a Christian, I am no longer under the curse of the law, this lingering 'itch' seems to have a voice of its own in reminding me of my crime.

It is for this reason, dear friends, that I have been much restricted in the use of my computer keyboard (it requiring for the most part the index finger of my right hand), and thus the writing of these 'blogs'.

On the plus side, I would appear to be 'on the mend' as regards this affliction, hence this missive.

As for my conscience (as frequently seems the case of late), I fear that we are not quite there yet.

Onward and upward
Derek

Mar

11

Happy birthday to me!
5 March, 2011

Dear Friends

It is indeed a day for much jubilation in that today marks the first anniversary of my entry into the 'blogosphere'.

Who would have believed that one so reticent with all things technological could have so readily mastered this popular medium of communication (alas, a turn of phrase that would not be one oft used by my congregation to describe my preaching style), and consistently turned out such a prolific output?

Your company along the way has been much appreciated, and I trust that you will 'stay the course' as I continue to give you a window into the world of St. Cliff's.

It is indeed my good fortune that I have been reading the book of Proverbs of late, and that the voice of wisdom (not my good lady wife on this occasion) caused my impatient hand to be stayed from an act of desperation. In a bid to increase the tally of my 'online' flock, I was rashly at the point of considering calling a day of prayer and fasting at St. Cliff's to aid my endeavours.

With my congregation of the airwaves growing apace as I sally forth into my second year on the 'blogosphere', such a high profile faux pas really is the last thing I need.

What would the bishop say?

Onward and upward
Derek

A glass of water is never quite enough for Derek!

Derek was evangelising in his sleep again!

Total immersion christenings are Derek's way of keeping a foot in both camps!

Derek was having that 'last page of the sermon is missing' dream again!

Derek probably wasn't using Powerpoint to it's full potential!

www.derekthecleric.com

If you've enjoyed this book then why not continue to follow Derek the Cleric on his brilliant new website? Become part of Derek's ever-growing online congregation and enjoy a regular dose of his light-hearted take on life.

This one-stop site for fun and entertainment is jam-packed with loads of comical features – all designed to put a smile on your face.

There are all your favourites, such as St. Cliff's Weekly News Sheet Highlights, 'Notes to Self', Letters, Photos, 'Ask Derek', not forgetting Derek's regular ramblings that allow you into the hallowed and hilarious precincts of St. Cliff's.

National Distributors

UK: (and countries not listed below)
CWR, Waverley Abbey House, Waverley Lane, Farnham, Surrey GU9 8EP.
Tel: (01252) 784700 Outside UK (44) 1252 784700 Email: mail@cwr.org.uk

AUSTRALIA: KI Entertainment, Unit 21 317-321 Woodpark Road, Smithfield,
New South Wales 2164. Tel: 1 800 850 777 Fax: 02 9604 3699
Email: sales@kientertainment.com.au

CANADA: David C Cook Distribution Canada, PO Box 98, 55 Woodslee Avenue, Paris,
Ontario N3L 3E5. Tel: 1800 263 2664 Email: sandi.swanson@davidccook.ca

GHANA: Challenge Enterprises of Ghana, PO Box 5723, Accra.
Tel: (021) 222437/223249 Fax: (021) 226227 Email: ceg@africaonline.com.gh

HONG KONG: Cross Communications Ltd, 1/F, 562A Nathan Road, Kowloon.
Tel: 2780 1188 Fax: 2770 6229 Email: cross@crosshk.com

INDIA: Crystal Communications, 10-3-18/4/1, East Marredpalli, Secunderabad – 500026,
Andhra Pradesh. Tel/Fax: (040) 27737145 Email: crystal_edwj@rediffmail.com

KENYA: Keswick Books and Gifts Ltd, PO Box 10242-00400, Nairobi.
Tel: (020) 2226047/312639 Email: sales.keswick@africaonline.co.ke

MALAYSIA: Canaanland, No. 25 Jalan PJU 1A/41B, NZX Commercial Centre, Ara Jaya,
47301 Petaling Jaya, Selangor.
Tel: (03) 7885 0540/1/2 Fax: (03) 7885 0545 Email: info@canaanland.com.my

Salvation Publishing & Distribution Sdn Bhd, 23 Jalan SS 2/64, 47300 Petaling Jaya,
Selangor. Tel: (03) 78766411/78766797 Fax: (03) 78757066/78756360
Email: info@salvationbookcentre.com

NEW ZEALAND: KI Entertainment, Unit 21 317-321 Woodpark Road, Smithfield,
New South Wales 2164, Australia. Tel: 0 800 850 777 Fax: +612 9604 3699
Email: sales@kientertainment.com.au

NIGERIA: FBFM, Helen Baugh House, 96 St Finbarr's College Road, Akoka, Lagos.
Tel: (01) 7747429/4700218/825775/827264 Email: fbfm_1@yahoo.com

PHILIPPINES: OMF Literature Inc, 776 Boni Avenue, Mandaluyong City.
Tel: (02) 531 2183 Fax: (02) 531 1960 Email: gloadlaon@omflit.com

SINGAPORE: Alby Commercial Enterprises Pte Ltd, 95 Kallang Avenue #04-00,
AIS Industrial Building, 339420. Tel: (65) 629 27238 Fax: (65) 629 27235
Email: marketing@alby.com.sg

SOUTH AFRICA: Struik Christian Books, 80 MacKenzie Street, PO Box 1144,
Cape Town 8000. Tel: (021) 462 4360 Fax: (021) 461 3612
Email: info@struikchristianmedia.co.za

SRI LANKA: Christombu Publications (Pvt) Ltd, Bartleet House, 65 Braybrooke Place,
Colombo 2. Tel: (9411) 2421073/2447665 Email: dhanad@bartleet.com

USA: David C Cook Distribution Canada, PO Box 98, 55 Woodslee Avenue, Paris, Ontario
N3L 3E5, Canada. Tel: 1800 263 2664 Email: sandi.swanson@davidccook.ca

CWR is a Registered Charity – Number 294387
CWR is a Limited Company registered in England – Registration Number 1990308